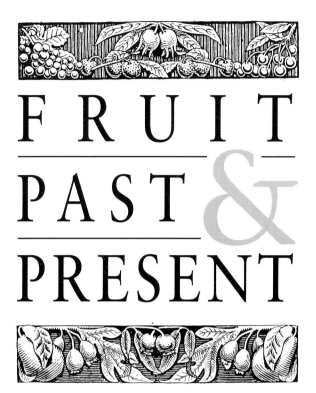

FRUIT
PAST & PRESENT
PRESENT

Edited for the RHS by Karen Wilson

Honorary Editor for the Fruit Group: Brian Self

The RHS Fruit Group Committee
Chairman: P Blackburne-Maze
Vice-Chairman: H A Baker
Members: Miss S Baxter, D W Burd, P Dodd, G M Edwards, E G Gilbert,
J H C Sale, R Sanders, B F Self, R Sherman, P E Smith, E Spanier, H F Stringer,
P J Woodward
Secretary: Mrs M Sweetingham

Designed by Graham Dudley Associates, Hanworth, Middx

Printed by The KPC Group, London and Ashford, Kent

front cover: clockwise from top left Redcurrant (copyright Jerry Harpur); Apple 'Bramley's Seedling' (copyright Photos Horticultural); Cherry 'Bigarreau Napolean' (copyright Andrew Lawson); Pear 'Conference' (copyright Eric Crichton)

back cover: top Cherry 'Morello';
bottom Pear 'Williams' Bon Chrétien' (copyright RHS)

Contents

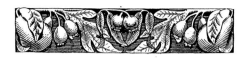

FOREWORD *by Brian Self*	5
MEDLEY OF MEMORIES *by Christopher Hatton*	7
HISTORY OF THE FRUIT GROUP	9
THE GOLDEN YEARS OF FRUIT *by Jack Woodward*	10
THE RHS FRUIT GROUP INVADE FRANCE *by Peter Blackburne-Maze*	14
VINE TRAINING FOR THE GREENHOUSE *by Ray Waite*	18
COMMERCIAL VINE GROWING *by Sheila Baxter*	22
SUCCESS WITH SEEDLESS *by Peter Bauwens*	25
GRAPES GONE TO POT *by Ray Waite*	29
FLAVOURSOME FRUITS *by Harry Baker*	33
FRUIT TREE ROOTSTOCKS *by Tony Webster*	37
CORDON PLUMS FOR THE SMALL GARDEN *by Gerald Edwards*	51
CHANGING DESIGNS FOR ORCHARDS *by Peter Dodd*	53

continued overleaf

DO WINDBREAKS IMPROVE FRUIT? *by Sheila Baxter*   59

HONEYBEES AND POLLINATION *by Karl Showler*   62

BROGDALE HORTICULTURAL TRUST *by Joan Morgan*   67

IN SEARCH OF 'WARRIOR' *by John Sale*   72

WISLEY'S MODEL GARDENS *by Jim Arbury*   74

SCOTTISH SOFT FRUIT BREEDING DEVELOPMENTS
by Ronnie McNicol   79

PRIMOCANE FRUITING RASPBERRIES *by Victoria Knight*   84

GROWING STRAWBERRIES ON RAISED BEDS *by Sheila Baxter*   90

PEST AND DISEASE MANAGEMENT IN COMMERCIAL
FRUIT PRODUCTION *by Angela Berrie and Jerry Cross*   93

FIRST AID FOR FRUIT *by Pippa Greenwood*   103

FRUIT THE NATURAL WAY *by Bob Sherman*   106

THE DEVELOPMENT OF PEST AND DISEASE
RESISTANCE IN APPLES AT HRI *by Frank Alston*   110

CUCKOO IN JUNE *by David Atkins*   113

OUR EUROPEAN COUNTERPARTS *by Howard Stringer*   117

REFLECTIONS ON FRUIT *by Bob Sanders*   121

INDEX   126

Foreword

THE FRUIT GROUP of the Royal Horticultural Society was established in response to representations by professional and amateur fruit enthusiasts led by Dr (later, Sir Ronald) Hatton in 1945. Sir Ronald was the Group's founder and first Chairman as well as Director of East Malling Research Station and a keen gardener.

He was a skilled communicator and did much to ensure that the results of research were passed on to the fruit industry, to benefit both the commercial and amateur grower.

The strength of the Group has been its close liaison with its members. Every year there have been opportunities for visits, talks and discussions in the programme of events. The emphasis has, perhaps, been on the spoken rather than the written word; not that the Group's publications have been insignificant! Members of the Group prepared the initial version of *The Fruit Garden Displayed*, first published by the Society in 1951. This concise and well-recommended guide to fruit culture in the garden has been revised at intervals and is still going strong in its 8th edition.

In the past the Group produced Yearbooks which contained a selection of articles, many of which would merit re-reading today. In 1966 an occasional publication *Fruit Present and Future* was produced to celebrate the Group's 21st birthday. Subsequently, a second volume, published under the same title in 1973, reviewed advances in fruit science and culture.

This book, in celebration of 50 years of the RHS Fruit Group, has a diverse variety of topics; some are research reviews, others cover cultural techniques and the experiences of amateur growers. I am grateful to all who have kindly contributed to this 50th anniversary volume, either by writing or assisting in its production.

In dedicating this publication to Sir Ronald Hatton, the founder of the RHS Fruit Group, I know he would have been pleased to learn of its production and delighted at the progress and success of 'his' Group.

BRIAN SELF
Honorary Editor and former Chairman, RHS Fruit Group

A *Medley of Memories*

By Christopher Hatton

IT IS AT ONCE a great privilege and pleasure to be invited to write for this production to celebrate the 50th anniversary of the RHS Fruit Group. I am in no position to share any scientific contribution, but I can offer you some of the memories I have from my boyhood days onward at East Malling.

It was, I think, in 1926 that we moved into the Great East, the new Director's house at East Malling Research Station, now Horticulture Research International (HRI). One of my most vivid memories and associations with that happy home is the considerable number of visitors who were entertained there. I had the privilege of getting to know great fruit farmers such as Percy Manwaring, Spencer Mount, Jimmy Robertson, Tom Neame, Alfred Day, Talbot Edmonds, Willy Rogers and also Professor Blackman and H V Taylor. People visiting the Research Station for the day often came along too. I remember visits from Kathleen Murray, Sir Daniel Hall and from public figures such as Malcolm Macdonald and Bert Hinkler (who hoped to get a job flying fruit around the globe!) There were the staff tennis tournaments with tea on the lawn and staff Christmas parties in the packing shed for which we used to ferry down large quantities of baked potatoes.

I remember the first root labora-tory being dug on the corner of plot 9 and the erection of the Manwaring Building which for a short time had a large veranda over the entrance. Each Sunday, after our return from Church in Maidstone, I used to accompany my father on a walk around all the various plots. Invariably we would meet Jesse Amos and his daughter Margaret doing the rounds as well. I am sure that it was during these guided tours that I picked up a great deal of my knowledge of fruit growing. Open Days were a delight and I took part in as many as I could. I well remember a 'Worcester Pearmain' day for which growers brought a sample of their crop to make a fascinating display of apples grown on different soils. The day was a great success but looking ahead one of the speakers thought 'one Derby Day in the year was sufficient'.

One of my lucky days was being given permission to escape from school to be present for the visit of the Duke of York in 1934. The Duke showed great personal interest in the work being done at East Malling and we were told that he would return for a private visit. Unfortunately public events prevented that taking place.

It was in 1937 that Sir John Ramskill Twisden of Bradbourne House died and my father told me to go on my bicycle to Sir John's relative, Miss Brennand, with

Sir Ronald Hatton founder of the Fruit Group

a letter asking permission for him to look around Bradbourne. That was the first of many visits to Bradbourne before it became part of the Research Station and the beginning of friendships with Mr and Mrs Phillips and Rayfield.

I look back on those boyhood years with immense happiness and also with great gratitude to all the staff who were so patient with me when I came and interrupted their work. Their kindness contributed to a little bit of fruit production in the North Riding. Fruit growing in monasteries goes back a long way - there is a well known map or plan of the monastery at St Gall in the Middle Ages with its apple trees planted in the cemetery! When I joined the Benedictine monks at Ampleforth there were a few apple trees planted around the turn of the century. It was not long before I was told to produce as many apples for as much of the year as possible. The market of some 800 staff and boys was on the doorstep. There was no apple

store with artificial cooling or controls, so a wide collection of cultivars was planted to discover which would flourish in the north and which would keep successfully under totally natural conditions. Eventually we planted about 2.5ha (6 acres) mainly on MM104 which about 10 years ago we started to grub and replace with spindle bushes on M9.

Time has passed and ways have parted: I am now working in a parish not far from Carlisle, but fruit growing is in my blood stream and so is my concern for what I still think of as East Malling Research Station. One of my vivid memories of the inter-war period was my father's continual concern with finance and his immense appreciation for the financial support from growers particularly for the donations enabling Bradbourne to be purchased. It seemed that money was always short and that puts limits on growth and research. With the advent of the Second World War came increased Government funding and rapid growth. Today I just find myself wondering whether in some way history is not repeating itself: government funding has been reduced and once again East Malling is looking to growers for its financial support.

I would like to conclude by offering my congratulations to the RHS Fruit Group on its 50th birthday and to wish all its members as much interest and joy as fruit growing has been to me.

CHRISTOPHER HATTON is the son of Sir Ronald Hatton. Father Edmund Hatton (as he is known in his monastery but in fruit circles is still Christopher) developed successful fruit orchards, in addition to his pastoral and teaching work, at Ampleforth College, Yorkshire, and is now responsible for a busy parish at Warwick Bridge, near Carlisle

History of the RHS Fruit Group

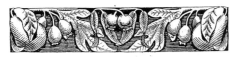

IN OCTOBER 1945 the inaugural meeting of the Fruit Group of the Royal Horticultural Society took place in London. Among the initial goals set by the RHS Fruit Group, and which today it continues to strive for are:

The desirability of a re-examination of old varieties as, with our present day knowledge of stocks, nutrition and pest control, they might get a much higher rating, especially in regard to their suitability for particular purposes, soils and conditions, and as potential parents of new varieties.

Drawing attention to the merits of little-known varieties

Making the results of research more widely known

Encouraging the 'great desire for knowledge of fruit growing among the owners of small gardens'

The annual programme originally consisted of four discussions (one per quarter), one arranged to coincide with the July fruit competition and another with the autumn fruit show, with excursions planned between meetings.

The first Chairman of the Fruit Group Committee, responsible for organising the Fruit Group, was Dr (later Sir) Ronald Hatton, Director of East Malling Research Station. Other founding members were N Bagenal, author of *Fruit Growing*; nurseryman A Cheal; H H Crane, author of *Fruit for Small Gardens*; geneticist M B Crane, co-author with Daniel Hall of *The Apple*; Sir Thomas Neame, fruit grower; market gardener F A Secrett; food and wine writer P Morton Shand; Fred Streeter, head gardener at Petworth, and Dr Thomas Wallace, Director of Long Ashton Research Station. By the appearance of the first Fruit Yearbook in 1947 the RHS Fruit Group had over 400 members. Today, as well as its increased membership meeting in the South-East, the Group also has an energetic West Midlands Branch as well as a newly formed South-West Branch.

The Group have always been very active in promoting fruit and instigated the publication by the RHS of *The Fruit Garden Displayed* in 1951. A request from the Group also led to the planting of three model fruit gardens at the RHS Garden Wisley and at East Malling Research Station, whose object was 'to show the amateur types of trees of restricted form which are suitable for planting in a small area, and how a fruit garden can be planned where space is limited'.

The Group assisted in the production of the Fruit Yearbooks from 1947 to 1958, and of the 21st anniversary publication *Fruit Present and Future* in 1966, and its sequel in 1973. More recently, in collaboration with the Fruit and Vegetable Committee, the Group helped to arrange the Fruit Conference and Exhibition in 1983. Today the Group continues to provide inspiration through a varied programme of lectures, discussions and visits to nurseries and gardens.

Chairmen of the RHS Fruit Group
1945 - 49 SIR RONALD HATTON
1949 - 64 DR H V TAYLOR, former Horticultural Commissioner for the Ministry of

Agriculture
1965 - 74 J M S POTTER, Director of the National Fruit Trials
1974 - 80 DR F R TUBBS, former Director of East Malling Research Station
1980 - 90 B F SELF
1990 - 93 P J WOODWARD
1993 to date P BLACKBURNE -MAZE

Adapted from a report by Brent Elliott, Librarian and Archivist for the Royal Horticultural Society

The Golden Years of Fruit

JACK WOODWARD

I SUPPOSE THOSE who live longest see most. During the past 50 years some aspects of fruit growing in the garden have changed, often dramatically. Some changes have been short lived; some subtle and enduring, others a rediscovery of old wisdoms. I always get the feeling that fruit growing goes in cycles, or perhaps circles!

There are three main aspects of fruit growing in gardens: plant material, growing practice and pests and diseases.

PLANT MATERIAL
The quality of the plant material pur-chased decides its cropping for years to come and in the case of soft fruits, its life expectancy. During the past 50 years the most important revolution has been in the introduction of virus-free material. The production of healthy plant material from the research stations and the certification of most soft fruits and the components of tree fruits has ensured that high quality plants and trees, true to name, have reached the gardener through retail outlets.

The benefits to the plant raiser are considerable, with the production of better trees and plants, and for gardeners yields are higher without the inhibiting effect of insidious viruses. Many viruses are not apparent in the host plant and their effects on cropping are only shown when comparative trials are made. Other viruses, like yellow edge and crinkle of strawberry, are obvious and debilitating in many cultivars and have led to the loss of many otherwise excellent cultivars such as 'Huxley', however, 'Royal Sovereign' has just about survived. The message today is always buy quality trees or plants, preferably with a certification guarantee.

Over the years many cultivars have come and gone whereas others have survived the test of time. Strawberries have changed most, apples least. Some cultivars have been like shooting stars, others like lead balloons. The strawberry 'Climax' promised to be the wonder of the age in the late 1940s and was indeed outstanding till it was suddenly devastated by the virus-like problem, June Yellows. I still feel that cultivar needed more investigation than it received. 'Domanil' was also affected and more recently, some stocks of 'Cambridge Favourite'. Of the many new strawberries, none will last as long as this reliable old cultivar, which has shown little sign of wilt or red core, grows under any conditions and hangs ripe on the plant for days. 'Cambridge Favourite' has lasted over 30 years, but will 'Elsanta' survive that long?

Very few of the new soft fruit cultivars have illuminated the garden but the raspberry 'Autumn Bliss' does that, and more. A good, well-flavoured berry, easy to grow, it is here to stay. Of all the other raspberries only 'Leo', which takes the old 'Norfolk Giant' slot, is outstanding. 'Malling Jewel' remains a jewel!

Among blackcurrants, old cultivars, with the exception of 'Baldwin', have disappeared commercially and are being replaced by those suitable for the juice industry. 'Ben Sarek' has fallen into the laps of the gardener; it has large berries, gives a heavy crop and makes a compact bush.

And what has happened to tree fruits in 50 years? The story here is a bit like the curate's egg, good in parts!

All the old apples are still about, Laxton's introductions, 'Bramley's Seedling' and 'Cox's Orange Pippin'. In the absence of wondrous new cultivars, we are turning back to good old ones. Nevertheless, some of the new cultivars have become favourites, such as 'Jonagold', 'Falstaff' and 'Greensleeves'. Discarded commercially, both 'Falstaff' and 'Greensleeves' have excellent garden qualities such as reliability and decent eating quality in season.

The pears we plant are still mainly 'Conference', 'Doyenné du Comice' and 'Williams' Bon Chrétien' because they are generally the most readily available. 'Conference' is an easy kind to grow, reliable and not too fussy about a pollinator, but more recently 'Concorde' has been attracting attention. Similar to 'Conference', it has better quality and performance.

The wealth of plum cultivars that we had 50 years ago seems to have shrunk to 'Victoria' and just one or two others. A few new ones have found a place, 'Marjorie's Seedling' among them. More recently there are hopes for new Long Ashton and Scandinavian cultivars. Unfortunately, the market for plums has declined and it seems to have reduced the interest shown by amateurs.

Cherries have become a brighter

prospect these days with self-fertile 'Stella' and the bacterial canker–resistant 'Merchant' available. The outlook is promising when you think of the large trees of 50 years ago and the problems of pollination. Birds still like cherries!

ROOTSTOCKS

As the size of gardens has decreased, so fruit trees have needed to become smaller. The large 'Bramley's Seedling' on M2 rootstock has no place in commerce or in the garden. For apples we now have M27, a super dwarfing rootstock which can squeeze a 'Bramley's Seedling' into the smallest garden. Miniature tree growing is now possible. The M9 rootstock which was used for dwarf trees 50 years ago has been freed from virus disease and is now more vigorous than of old. It can still be used for the less vigorous cultivars.

'Pixy', a dwarfing plum rootstock, makes a more manageable size of tree and renders the picking ladder obsolete. However, for a small tree with heavy cropping potential, it is important to reduce the crop loading severely by early thinning.

There has been considerable interest in producing dwarf rootstocks for cherries, but so far results have been disappointing. 'Colt' makes a smaller tree than F12/1, though it is still big by any standards. Hope springs eternal!

CULTIVATION

Not much has changed in the cultural management of fruit in the garden. Plastic has replaced heavy glass cloches in some gardens and growing strawberries in vertical containers has partly replaced pots in the greenhouse. Nothing changes: soft fruit is still grown chaotically in some gardens.

The techniques for pruning trees are more or less the same as those of 50 years ago, although the growing of spindle trees has had some influence on gardeners. Espaliers, dwarf pyramids, cordons and fan-shaped trees have remained unchanged. In the 1940s there were commercial plantings of cordons and dwarf pyramids, but these disappeared as the practice of growing big trees came in. Now some growers have discovered very intensive culture again! Many gardeners now grow dwarf trees in place of one or two large standards.

PESTS AND DISEASES

Fifty years ago we had lime sulphur, tar oil, nicotine, derris, lead arsenate and two bricks! Apart from derris (and the bricks), this was an unpleasant lot and not entirely satisfactory.

Lime sulphur was effective in controlling diseases such as apple scab and mildew and also pests like big bud mite of blackcurrant. Early sprays, pre-blossom on apple, could burn out primary mildew infections and also scorch early leaf. Many cultivars of apple and blackcurrant were so badly affected by lime sulphur they could not be sprayed with it and were said to be 'sulphur shy' – anybody who has used lime sulphur on an unsettled spring day can understand the meaning of this term! However, the big problem with sulphur was its effect on cropping and this was not really appreciated until new materials like captan and karathane replaced it in the 1950s. Crop yield rose considerably. Modern fungicides have continued to give a bonus to grower and gardener.

Tar oil killed aphid eggs and cleaned up trees but it also killed many predators of red spider mite, which became a summer menace. It could be said that tar oil started the problem of chemical resistance we have today.

Nicotine and lead arsenate were used in gardens and on commercial farms with gay abandon, but were replaced by DDT in the 1950s. DDT was then overtaken by 'safer' materials and now we have synthetic pyrethrins and more specific chemicals like pirimicarb which kill only aphids.

Parasites can be used for dealing with red spider mite, caterpillars and whitefly while predators are now encouraged since fewer and safer chemicals are being used.

The use of pheromone traps (sex attractants) for nasties such as codling moth has enabled gardeners not only to be warned of moth movements but to obtain effective control. Biological science has begun to open many doors for the amateur fruit grower, though it will require better understanding of proposed treatments.

Resistance of pests and diseases to chemicals is of greater concern to commercial growers, but the fall-out from their problems can affect the gardener too. In some cases mildew became resistant to benomyl on commercial farms and red spider mite became resistant to

a run of acaricides. It pays to be moderate and careful in the use of chemicals and choose the correct time to apply them. An early spray for mildew is often better than five sprays later on and ringing the changes is always a good thing.

Of more importance to the amateur is the resistance of plants to pests and diseases, such as the new raspberries for example, with their resistance to virus carrying aphids, and gooseberries like 'Invicta' and 'Greenfinch', which are resistant to American gooseberry mildew. Spraying has never been effective against bacterial canker of cherries but the resistance in 'Merton Glory' and the new cultivars such as 'Merchant' is a bonus. Apples resistant to apple scab and mildew have also been introduced in recent times, starting with the John Innes cultivar 'Gavin'.

As time goes by science will continue to introduce all sorts of possibilities. I look forward to growing the cultivars of the next decade; they will be easy to manage and productive, they will possess built in resistance to the major pests and diseases and bear quality fruit.

JACK WOODWARD is a former Chairman of the RHS Fruit Group. He serves on the RHS Fruit and Vegetable and Fruit Group Committees

The RHS Fruit Group Invade France

BY PETER BLACKBURNE-MAZE

APART FROM A VERY early start for some members, our departure from Victoria on 7 September, 1993, and the trip to Dover were uneventful. We caught the 11.15am ferry, the *Pride of Burgundy*, and were soon in France.

Our first stop was at the fruit farm of Pierre Dalle and his son Jean-Pierre at Saulty. Jean-Pierre spoke very good English but his father and mother, Françoise, none at all. They run a mixed fruit farm of about 20 ha (50 acres),12 ha (30 acres) of apples on M9, 'Jonagold', 'Jonagored', 'Gloster' and their best seller, 'Elstar', 5 ha (13 acres) of pears, mainly 'Conference', 'Doyenné du Comice' and 'Concorde', but also 'Williams' Bon Chrétien' and some 'Beurré Hardy'. The newer trees are on Quince C. There are also 2 ha (5 acres) of strawberries and 5,000 sq m (1¼ acres) of raspberries.

The fruit is sold in several ways, some through a wholesaler in Lille, some through supermarkets, but about half from house to house in the neighbourhood. They also sell from the farm gate. To achieve a good fruit size, the apple crop is singled and thinned in July to approximately half the set. 'Arlette' is grown as a pollinator and is sold straight off the trees to bring in instant cash. The Dalles are busily replacing old trees at the moment. There is a rule coming into force throughout the EC which allows grubbed fruit trees to be replaced but no increase in fruit area is allowed.

One of the Dalles' other enterprises is letting rooms in their small, but lovely, mini château. The whole area is steeped in World War I history. Arras was a crucial town in the battles. Vimy ridge, with its appalling carnage and mainly Canadian cemeteries, is only a few miles away.

The next day was the one we had all been waiting for: the whole point of the trip was to be realised. We were off to visit the Potager du Roi adjacent to the Château of Versailles.

We were greeted by Professor Regnard who had come all the way from Montpelier, in the south of France, to show us round the Potager. It covers over 9 ha (23 acres) and although literally the royal kitchen garden, it originally contained all the fruit, vegetables and ornamentals that would have been required by the Court at the Palace. The garden was commissioned by Louis XIV and was under construction from 1678-83. This was supervised by Jean-Baptiste La Quintinye (1624-1688), a friend of

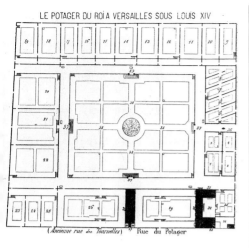

Plan of the Potager taken from Histoire de l'Ecole Nationale d'Horticulture *(1898)*

Le Nôtre. The design was, and still is, principally squares of vegetables surrounded by trained fruit trees; the smallest plot is some 500 sq m (600 sq yd). The central section, the Grand Carée, is made up of the original 16 squares of ornamentals, vegetables and fruit, each contained within vertically and horizontally trained espaliers, cordons, palmettes and palmette verriers; even some vases and arches.

The King's favourite vegetables and fruits were asparagus, peas, strawberries, figs, pears, plums and cantaloupe melons. This led to the creation of a 'figgery' and a 'melonnière'. Today, the fruit in the garden consists of 35 apple cultivars, 30 of pear as well as peaches, apricots, cherries, blackberries, quinces and even kiwis. This usually produces 50 to 60 tonnes of fruit a year.

When the garden was commissioned in the 17th century, the land was poor and boggy, described at the time as a 'stinking marsh'. It took five years to bring the soil into cultivation and involved draining the land into what is now the Pièce d'eau des Suisses. An added difficulty with the construction was that the whole garden area had to be sunken to create enough retaining walls to accommodate the trained fruit trees. Draining such an area and then excavating it was no mean feat. Originally, the trees were held in position by tying them with cotton strips nailed to the walls. This was replaced by strained wires in the 18th century.

Today, the garden and its accompanying buildings are part of the Versailles estate and are used to house L'Ecole Nationale Supérieure d'Horticulture. Very little experimental work goes on there but much use is made of modern methods and new cultivars to keep up to date and improve the economics.

The crop of 'Doyenné du Comice' in 1993 was rather disappointing. The main planting of these is as five-tier contra (in the open) espaliers, that is, in two rows either side of a path. Most of the pears are on the Quince Fontenay rootstock, similar in vigour to Quince A.

Unfortunately, some of the horizontal cordon apples, such as 'Golden Delicious' grafted on M9, are almost certainly virus infected.

Red spider mite is a constant menace, as we saw, and very little can be done about it. Resistance to organophosphorus insecticides is well established and natural predators cannot possibly keep them in check.

It was particularly interesting, but disheartening, to hear that they have just the same problems with bureaucracy at the Potager as we do in the United Kingdom. Another transfer is imminent with no prospects of a more

An illustration of pear palmettes and three rows of single tear apple espaliers from L'Ecole Nationale d'Horticulture *(1890)*

settled future. Shades of Brogdale, but with a French accent! However, the Potager cannot be replaced. It represents a national and living monument and should be treated as such. Professor Regnard spoke excellent English and gave us a fascinating and enjoyable tour.

Le Potager du Roi is open to the public at 2.30pm every afternoon except Mondays and Tuesdays.

Following some wonderful sightseeing expeditions to Monet's garden at Giverny, the famous Rungis food market and the majestic Château of Chantilly, we paid a visit on the third day to the nursery and fruit farm started and built up by the late Charles André which is now run by Bruno Essler. The nursery, Pépinières du Valois, is near the town of Villers Cotterets, north east of Paris.

This is the biggest fruit nursery in Europe and we were shown things that many of our newer and younger members had never seen before: trees that had just been budded, year-old trees and older ones that were being kept for special orders.

About 150 ha (370 acres) are planted, consisting of commercial orchard, nursery and trial grounds for cultivars. It is increasing at about 50 ha (125 acres) a year. There is a permanent staff of 55, which is increased to 120 during the budding season.

The fruit crop in 1993 was about average, except for the rather poor showing of 'Doyenné du Comice' and the light crop of the biennial apple 'Reinette du Canada' ('Grise du Canada'), which was in its off year.

The fruiting pear plantings are of 'Williams' Bon Chrétien', 'Conference', 'Concorde' and 'Doyenné du Comice'. The most important apples are 'Gala', 'Braeburn' and 'Jonagold' with 'Fuji' just coming into bearing. The significance of the cultivar trials is important. New cultivars, including several irradiated mutants, are grown to judge their commercial value. Those showing promise are built up in the nursery.

Unfortunately, another of the thunderstorms that plagued the trip burst upon us so things became rather confused towards the end of the afternoon. Kindness and helpfulness were everywhere and, once the tour of the orchard and nursery was over, we were treated to a superb champagne-cider that warmed the body and dulled the senses. It was of the well-known French sort that creeps up behind you and kicks you in the back of the knees!

The thirst quenching was continued that evening at an excellent dinner at the Maison du Vigneron, a well-known restaurant in the hills above Reims. It is no coincidence that it was in the heart of the Champagne country.

The previous evening proved to have been a mere hint for what was to follow on our fourth day. We went by coach up into the Champagne hills where we visited the vineyard of Didier Rothier in the village of Villers Marmery. This is near the appropriately named village of Bouzy. The grapes on this famous north-facing slope stretch as far as you can see.

M. Rothier and his young family only grow about 3 ha (8 acres) of Chardonnay grapes but make a comfortable living. The other Champagne grape is the better known 'Pinot Noir'.

The comparatively high price paid for the juice is because it is blended with that from the rest of their co-operative and sent to Moet to be made into champagne. Some is kept to make his own Blanc de Blancs. A quota system exists

so that there is no over production and after that quota of grapes for the year has been picked, the remainder is left to rot on the vines. That was his story, anyway! In 1993, picking was due to start on 13 September. Didier Rothier uses a locally converted tractor to do all the routine jobs among the vines.

The first thing that we learned about champagne is that black grapes such as 'Pinot Noir' will produce perfectly good white champagne provided that the skins are not crushed.

Making champagne is a skilled job and consists of two distinct operations. First, the juice from the grapes is fermented in vats. Each batch from the different vineyards is fermented separately. This represents many thousands of distinct wines but all have something in common: they are white and they are still. After fermentation, the different wines are blended. This goes on usually until March before the cellarmasters are satisfied with what they have created. This stage of champagne making is called the 'cuvée' and ends with suitable batches being blended together in the right proportions.

The next step is the second fermentation. For this, the wine is bottled and a mixture of wine, sugar and yeast is added to each bottle, which is then stopped with a strong crown cork. The second fermentation can take anything up to three months to finish but, however long it takes, the wine is kept for at least a further year. During this time, the bottle is gradually turned and inverted so that all the sediment settles down in the neck.

At the appointed time, the bottles, still upside down, are dipped in freezing brine until the sludge in the neck has

turned into ice. The bottle is then turned upright, the cap is flipped off and the icy plug of wine and sediment shoots out like a bullet. The bottle is topped up, corked, wrapped and is then ready for sale. Needless to say, all this listening was thirsty work and we did not wish to cause offence to M. Rothier by refusing his kind offer to sample his own champagne. I am told that it was a

very educational and memorable visit.

Anything after that was apt to be an anticlimax but we spent a most enjoyable hour or so over lunch and a short shopping session at a hypermarket on the way to Calais for the ferry.

Let us hope that this was the first of many outrageously successful Fruit Group trips abroad.

PETER BLACKBURNE-MAZE, a horticultural consultant and writer, is Chairman of the RHS Fruit Group and a member of the Society's Fruit and Vegetable Committee

Vine Training for the Greenhouse

RAY WAITE

IN THE HEYDAY of the private estate the culture of grapes under greenhouse conditions was brought to a high state of perfection, it being standard practice in larger establishments to have separate vineries for early, mid season and late

fruiting cultivars. Even today it is surprising to find grapes being successfully grown in quite small greenhouses and conservatories by amateur gardeners.

With the vagaries of the British climate most dessert grapes need the protection of glass to ripen properly. Certain cultivars, 'Muscat of Alexandria' for example, require artificial heat particularly at flower time to aid good pollination and also in the autumn to ensure perfect maturity.

Traditionally vineries were lean-to structures facing south, with a long sloping roof providing as large an area as possible for training the vines. However, vines can be successfully grown in a free-standing span structure such as the one at the Royal Horticultural Society's Wisley Garden or indeed the amateur's small greenhouse. When growing in the latter it is generally easier to bring the main stem – usually referred to as the rod – along the ridge of the greenhouse rather than training it vertically up the roof as done in a traditional vinery. It has to be said however that the latter is more easily managed.

Vines can be grown with or without artificial heat but the former guarantees an earlier crop as it is possible to start early fruiting cultivars into growth during February so that they can ripen during August or even earlier. In a cold greenhouse growth will start naturally in March or April with harvesting somewhat later depending on the season.

For best results, particularly in heated greenhouses, plant vines in a specially constructed border. This gives the grower greater control. However, vines planted with their roots outside the greenhouse are easier to manage and will be satisfactory especially if the crop is grown unheated. In this case an early-maturing cultivar is ideal.

Ensure the planting site is well drained. An outside border must be thoroughly cultivated and prepared with extra drainage material. This will also be required for an inside border and in addition it may be necessary to provide for land drains so that excess water is discharged outside the greenhouse.

Under glass the newly planted young vine will not need an extensive root run in its early years and the standard practice of constructing a narrow border and adding to the width over a period of years is ideal. The front edge of the border can be retained by bricks, concrete blocks or planking and the border should be 60cm to 1m (2-3ft) deep.

Fix support wires horizontally along the length of the greenhouse starting about 1m (3ft) off the ground and continuing at intervals of 23 to 30cm (9 to 12in) apart, keeping the wires 38 to 45cm (15 to 18in) away from the glass. Having said that, in a small greenhouse it is not very practicable for the wires to be too far away from the glass, but as the young vine shoots grow vertically they will soon stub themselves against the glazing and become distorted or even scorched if too close. It is important too to have a good circulation of air between the glass and the foliage.

Traditionally vines were planted 1.2m (4ft) apart and grown vertically on what is known as the rod and spur systems allowing the laterals to extend about 60cm (2ft) on either side of the rod. In the small greenhouse it is more feasible to plant a single vine at the gable end away from the door and train the rod horizontally under the ridge.

Newly planted vines should be pruned back fairly hard in the dormant season as it is important to obtain vigorous growth. During the first season it is possible to have at least 3m (10ft) of main stem produced which must be cut

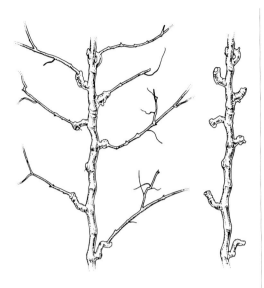

The rod and spur system of pruning – before (left) and after (right) pruning immediately after leaf fall.

back by two thirds during the next dormant period. This technique is carried out each year until the rod has reached the topmost wire. During this time prune back the side shoots to one or two buds (or eyes). These will form spurs on which subsequent yearly shoots will bear fruit.

In a heated structure mid-February is a good time to start early-fruiting cultivars into growth. Lower the vine so that the tip of the rod is bent over and almost touching the greenhouse floor; this slows the upward movement of sap and therefore ensures that the spurs break into growth as evenly as possible. At this time regular spraying with clear water helps growth to break freely. When the rod has produced a full complement of shoots tie it back up to the wires. At this stage it is important that temperatures do not rise excessively so

carefully ventilate the greenhouse and keep temperatures at about 19°C (66°F). Leave one lateral to each spur so that the wires are completely covered. As these laterals will try to grow vertically tie them down to the horizontal wires very carefully as it is easy for them to snap at the junction with the older wood. Do this in the morning as later in the day the shoots, although limp and therefore easily managed, become charged with sap and can easily break.

After five leaves, flower trusses will form so pinch the lateral two leaves beyond the flower and allow growth to extend as far as is necessary to cover the wires. Some cultivars set their fruit very freely and I would recommend these for general purposes. Such cultivars as 'Black Hamburgh', 'Foster's Seedling' and 'Buckland Sweetwater' do not need any special attention other than a vigorous shake during the early afternoon to ensure pollination. Shy setters like the Muscat types should have pollen transferred from the stamens to receptive stigmas either by using a rabbit's tail or cupped hands. At this stage it is essential to keep the greenhouse atmosphere as dry as possible.

The number of bunches left to fruit must be regulated as the aim is to retain approximately half a kilo (1 lb) of fruit for every 30cm (1ft) run of rod. Thin the grapes within the bunch with either grape thinning scissors or ordinary sharply pointed scissors and use a small forked stick to manipulate the fruit. Never touch the grapes with your fingers as this damages the translucent waxy covering on the berries, known as the bloom, and disfigures the bunch and removes the water repellent. Thinning is largely a matter of experience

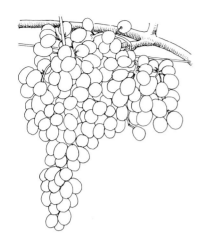 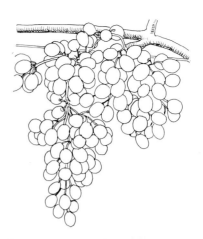

Bunches before (left) and after (right) second thinning.

and it is not uncommon to remove half the berries. Remove grapes formed in the middle of the bunch first and then any undersized fruit and finally the outer ones. This can be carried out in more than one stage. Thinning is essential otherwise the berries become too congested and split and rot.

A vine in full growth will make heavy demands on soil moisture especially in hot weather so vines with their roots outside may require watering every seven to 10 days provided the drainage is adequate. When roots are confined to an inside border, mulching with straw will do nothing but good and for good quality fruit regularly apply a high potash fertilizer. If, however, growth is not vigorous, apply a general feed or one with a higher nitrogen content for early growth in spring.

Throughout the growing season remove any new shoots not required to fill gaps on the wires and remove growing tips on all sub laterals after one leaf.

All tendrils must be removed as soon as they appear. When the grapes start to ripen it is important to keep a much drier atmosphere to reduce the risk of splitting the berries. Keep the top ventilators slightly open at night so that the air temperature the following morning does not rise too rapidly.

Even when the grapes are well coloured it will be some time before they are really ripe; this finishing period varies with the cultivar and time of year. Early-fruiting ones, such as 'Black Hamburgh' and 'Foster's Seedling', need only three or four weeks to fully ripen whereas later ones, and in particular 'Muscat of Alexandria', can remain on the vine for up to 10 weeks before they are at their best. At harvesting time cut the bunch leaving a small length of branch either side of the stem to act as a handle. This aids manipulation and ensures that the fruits will not be marked if any bad berries have to be removed.

RAY WAITE is Superintendent of Glasshouses at the RHS Garden Wisley

Commercial Vine Growing

SHEILA BAXTER

POSSIBLY THE MOST notable thing that has taken place in commercial vine growing in Britain has been the vast increase in the area planted since the early 1970s. At that time there was only a small amount of commercial vine growing (no figures are available), but after two warm summers in the mid 1970s there was an explosion of interest and by 1986 there were 488 ha (1,205 acres) under cultivation. By 1994 there were over 1,000 ha (2,470 acres) – a 51 per cent increase in eight years!

This increase in acreage represents a very considerable investment, especially where vines are planted on the intensive Double Guyot system at 3,333 per hectare (1,349 per acre). Even the less intensive Geneva Double Curtain system at 1,106 per hectare (448 per acre) is not cheap, when you consider the cost of planting and establishing a vineyard. For the Double Guyot system it costs around £5,000 per hectare (that is, over £2,000 an acre) and this is just for the first year. It is over £5,600 per hectare £2,280 per acre) if the four establishment years are included.

The rather frightening thing is the way some people have plunged blithely into vine growing in order to produce wine, but without seeking proper advice about the suitability of the site or the soil, or the cost involved in establishing a vineyard, let alone realising when they can expect some return from their massive investment. This is because few people going in for vine growing have any knowledge of horticulture (or agriculture), but simply enjoy gardening and fancy the outdoor life. Few, therefore, have any understanding of vine growth or appreciate the necessity, or ways, of controlling growth and cropping. Often they have just decided that they want to grow vines because they want to sell their own wine, so they go ahead – and then run for help when things go wrong!

It makes life more interesting for advisers, but it is sad to see people throwing money away on an ill-fated venture. It can take seven or more years of pocket-emptying before the costs are covered and some money starts to trickle back, and that represents a lot of capital tied up for a long time. The vineyard may never manage to make a profit if money for establishing it has to be borrowed and a horrible downward spiral can sadly end in bankruptcy.

Fortunately not everyone finds the learning stage too difficult, especially if they already have some knowledge of fruit growing, or go on viticulture training courses. Though there is little room for mistakes, many people end up running successful vineyards.

The speed of return on capital depends on two things – regular, reasonable crops and selling wine direct to the public. Tourism can be the icing on the cake, but it can also make the difference between profit and loss.

Anyone who has grown vines will know of their erratic performance in Britain. They are very dependent on warm, sunny weather from flowering (late June to late July, depending on the season) until picking (from September to November), to build up enough sugars to ripen the fruit sufficiently for a decent wine to be the end result. Warmth and sunshine are crucial during flowering, not only to set the crop for that year, but to initiate flowers for the following season. No sun equals little or no fruit next year.

In the autumn the big problem is cool, wet weather, which is an open invitation to our old enemy, the fungal infection botrytis, to rot the fruit – often before it is ripe. Little can be done to prevent it, other than removing the leaves around the bunches before ripening to allow plenty of air movement. No fungicides can be used for several weeks before harvest because they affect fermentation, so once again there may be little or no fruit.

This can spell disaster for the grower, especially if several bad years follow one another, as happened the few years before the hot summer of 1989.

The kind of botrytis infection which causes 'noble rot', affecting grapes left late on the vine and giving rise to some of the high quality sweet wines on the Continent, rarely occurs in Britain. It is dependent on a combination of the right climatic conditions and thin-skinned cultivars, which allows fruit infection at night, then drying during the day, so that sugars are concentrated.

Prospective growers should be told that, however good their site, they can expect no crop at all in three years out of 10 and they will be lucky if they have three good years in that 10!

It is because of this need for warmth and sunshine that most of our vineyards are in the southern counties, though odd areas with a warm microclimate can be found much further north. However, it is not just the microclimate that makes a good vineyard - the grower concerned must understand viticulture and also be (or employ) a good wine maker. Where vineyards are not big enough to justify the expense of a winery or the grower is not interested in wine making, other vineyards with wineries will make wine under contract for the grower and return it bottled. Some will buy the grapes to make their own wine, but growing grapes under a long-term, fixed-price contract for a winery can be financially risky.

The most successful growers combine good growing, good wine making, selling directly to the public and tourism. On the business side, the grower has to deal with VAT and the Customs and Excise Department as well as the licensing authorities if wine is to be drunk on the premises.

One aspect about commercial vine growing that few people know about is the fact that both the growing of vines and the making of wine come under EC legislation with its endless rules. The Ministry of Agriculture, Fisheries and Food has a Wines Branch which negotiates on behalf of British growers on the

Wine Management Committee in Brussels, but they have a very tough job in the face of long established wine producing countries such as France, Spain and Italy. Every area of vines planted which exceeds $\frac{1}{4}$ hectare (1 acre) has to be registered with the Wine Standards Board.

For many years vine growers in the United Kingdom have thought of themselves as having 'experimental' status in the EC, but this has never been the case even though they have experimented widely in the number of kinds grown – over 50 of them! Officially, they are only permitted to grow certain types of grape to make into wine for sale in the EC. These fall into the following categories:

Recommended varieties, which are normally expected to produce good quality wine.

Authorised varieties, which are expected to make sound, marketable wines, but of a lower quality than that from Recommended varieties.

Provisionally Authorised varieties which allow varieties that appear to be useful after five years of trials to be added provisionally to the Authorised Group. After a further five to seven years of trials they can be moved into the Recommended or Authorised Groups, or dropped.

Experimental varieties, where they are part of approved trials
Temporarily Authorised varieties, which produce lower quality wine that can only be used as a Table Wine. In the United Kingdom, these varieties are all those that were being grown on 31 December, 1976 which were not on the Recommended, Authorised, Provisionally Authorised or Experimental

lists and have not been up-graded. They have to be grubbed out by 31 December, 2001 and they may not be planted, re-planted or grafted. These rules also apply to any variety that is down-graded to this category, though they can be grown for 25 years after they have been down-graded.

Much has been said lately about the use of hybrids, or inter-specific crosses as they are more correctly known. The best known of these is 'Seyval' (*Vitis vinifera* variety x *V. labrusca*), which can produce good quality wines in Britain. Unfortunately it produces large quantities of poor quality wine in the more southerly continental vineyards, so has gained a bad name for itself and inter-specific crosses in general. Because of this they may not be used in Quality Wine production. A battle royal is in progress to get the EC rules changed, as there are many new inter-specific crosses coming out of German breeding programmes, which could be very useful over here.

The big bonus with these cultivars (mostly *V. vinifera* varieties x *V. amurensis*) is their superb disease resistance and some of the newer cultivars are so good that it is difficult to tell their wine from those of *V. vinifera*, which are the only ones permitted in Quality Wine at present. However, it will surely not be long before public pressure against the use of pesticides will allow these hybrids to be used in Quality Wine.

Another piece of unwelcome legislation is the fact that Britain could be faced with a planting ban once production exceeds 25,000 hectolitres. This is because of over production of wine in the EC in general.

Policing of the legislation is undertaken by the Wine Standards Board of the Vintners Company and they maintain the United Kingdom Vineyard Register, which we were obliged to compile once the UK's vineyard area exceeded 500 hectares (1,235 acres). EC inspectors are allowed to see the Register and visit vineyards if they wish to check vineyard returns.

Needless to say, all these rules and regulations do not apply to amateur growers, but they do make the life of the commercial grower more complicated.

SHEILA BAXTER, a former member of the Ministry's Advisory Service (ADAS), is a member of the RHS Fruit Group Committee

Success with Seedless Grapes

PETER BAUWENS

OUR INTEREST in seedless grapes grew out of frustration when our two-year-old son refused to eat our fine outdoor grown grapes. At that time we grew a white Chasselas hybrid 'Witte van der Laan' and 'Boskoop Glory', two traditional Belgian outdoor cultivars, both reliable, well flavoured and early maturing. Admittedly the berries were rather small, but they tasted very nice, nothing that could surely displease the little fellow. But the small berries had rather big seeds and we found that he preferred his berries de-seeded. We have always believed in the innocent judgement of children and decided that he had made a point, so we started looking for seedless grapes. We knew some cultivars from the shops and took up the challenge of growing them ourselves.

Today our son is nine and we have built up a collection of about 50 seedless cultivars, half of them at the fruiting stage. We have not acquired many years of experience, but enough to check what we have read in publications and more than enough to get enthusiastic.

Seedless grapes hardly need any introduction, we all know them in dried form as raisins and currants. For dried fruit, seedlessness is even more important. 'Thompson Seedless' from California and 'Black Corinth' from Greece are the most famous ones. The fact that there are many more cultivars, most of them grown for the fresh fruit trade, is less known. We find 'Himrod' and 'Red Flame' in local shops, sometimes 'Thompson Seedless' as imports from Chile, South Africa and Israel, but somehow these cultivars have not become known to us as actual fruits to grow.

Belgium has a reputation for first class, giant glasshouse grapes and all the Italian imported fruits have much larger berries than the seedless ones. Although 'Ruby Seedless' and 'Emerald Seedless' have reasonably sized fruits, they have never become commercially popular as greenhouse cultivars. On the other hand, in outdoor cultivars, seedless grapes compare in size with their seeded cousins. So we decided that this was the direction in which to go, looking for well flavoured, healthy and early-maturing selections. As an extra, we found lots of diversity in appearance (colour, size, bunches, berry shape); ripening season (from August up to October) and of course flavour, from plain Sweetwater, through spicy, Muscat and foxy, up to rich and fruity.

When A F Barron wrote his *Vines and Vine Culture* in 1883, he made up a small list of six cultivars of 'Grapes of Peculiar Interest'. Two of them were seedless, namely 'Black Corinth' and 'Black Monukka'. This shows the early interest in seedlessness, it being not just a commercial novelty. Seedlessness is found in the European *Vitis vinifera* as well as in the American *V. labrusca* and hybrids combining the fine flavour of the former with the health and vigour of the latter seem to be ideal.

THE TRIALS

We started collecting material in 1986. Plants, but mostly cuttings, were obtained from Belgium, Holland, England and France. We soon found that the most important sources were in the USA and we received most material from there. Later on we got contacts and propagation material from Italy and Germany. Commercial nurseries, private persons as well as official institutes supplied us with material.

The plants were grown in containers for the first season and planted out in autumn, with a protection of straw during the first two winters. So far we have not found any winter damage; we found some records on winter hardiness, some cultivars could get problems with -15°C (5°F), others have been reported hardy down to -30°C(-22°F). All plants are grown on their own roots and are planted out in very light, sandy, slightly alkaline soil. Before planting we dig holes 50cm (20in) wide and up to 1m (3ft) deep and fill them with a mixture of top soil, some very well decayed compost, bone meal, ground chalk and vermiculite.

We started planting out in a very sheltered site along a concrete wall, 1.8m (6ft) high, facing south-south-west, planting distance being 2m (6½ft). At the same time we planted some early and late cultivars in an old greenhouse in order to compare ripening under different conditions. Secondary plantings were made on the same site, but in an east-west direction in the open. These plants will probably fruit next season. The latest planting of new, very early and rather late cultivars were made under the protection of some white woven plastic foil; an experiment to find out how the plants grow under these conditions. It gives some frost protection in early spring to early cultivars, extra heat during summer for late cultivars, a lot of wind protection and some rain cover in autumn and frost and wind protection during the winter months.

These plants are expected to fruit

within a season or so. Plants are trailed along three wires along the wall, we use the umbrella and four cane 'kniffen system', letting the vines grow like a spreading bush.

Much importance is put into the health care of the plants. As certified organic growers, we know the importance of good cultivation. The soil, which seems well suited to grapes and the very protected site in which they are grown are two solid basics to start with. However, we do have problems with young plants in their first two years probably caused by the extremely dry soil, but the plants become very vigorous in the following years.

Twice over these years we had some minor problems with grapevine downy mildew, *Plasmopara viticola.* In the last extremely wet spring, this was solved by cutting off some of the infected leaves. Annual feeding is rather low, using 2 litres (70 fl oz) of worm-made compost in early spring. Winter handling consists of a simple pressure spraying with sieved and strained calcified seaweed.

In spring, early summer and late summer we give the plants three sprayings at weekly intervals with a liquid seaweed solution as a foliar feed and preventative health treatment. Seaweed products provide immediate feeding and extra protection. The earliest plants start to bud mid-April (the greenhouse-grown cultivars are about two weeks earlier), so there is a frost danger period of about one month. The young buds can withstand regular April frost but problems sometimes occur when warm weather in April makes for early leafing and early May brings an unexpected serious frost. We cover the plants with blankets in such a case – twice in the last

seven years. Blossoming occurs from mid-June onwards and the first fruits are ready mid-August, the greenhouse ones two weeks earlier. The difference between a good and warm summer, compared to a cold and wet season, is also two weeks and of course a bad season will bring problems for late outdoor types, the fruit of which will probably end up unripe.

Our grape season starts the second half of August when three of the very early cultivars compete for the first ripe bunch. Often the one best exposed to the sun wins, so we can say that 'Interlaken', 'Perlette' and 'Himrod' are equally early. They are also equal in berry size – rather small that is – similar in colour – yellowish-white – and flavour. The main difference lies in cluster size, 'Perlette' having very nice clusters but needing a little thinning or the bunches get too tight. 'Interlaken' has smaller bunches, while 'Himrod' has more irregular and loose bunches. The first two need more precise pruning while 'Himrod' is the easiest. All three have very sweet, neutral flavoured, crunchy little berries with thin and adherent skin, the two qualities found in most other seedless varieties. They are real delights to have, especially as early as August when a refreshing berry is always appreciated.

In early September we get the first blue grapes. 'Glenora' has medium-sized berries, loose medium-sized bunches, is moderately early with a slightly foxy, or typical Labrusca taste. 'Mars' ripens at the same time, same berry size, smaller bunches but more pronounced Labrusca, without getting too extreme in taste. Both are slip-skin (non-adherent) with a thicker skin than other seedless grapes, resulting in better keeping quality; 'Mars' especially holds on the vine, even to the end of October.

Many people in Europe still consider Labrusca flavour, or foxiness, a disadvantage. We do agree that some American types have an extreme pronounced flavour, unlikely to attract many people to grow them. But just like our European Muscat flavour, just a little bit of Labrusca in the flavour can open up a whole new world. 'Venus', with blue to bronze-coloured fruits, is such an example of new and surprising taste; some Labrusca, some Muscat, but altogether very fruity, with a hint of strawberry or raspberry. It has medium to somewhat large berries, nice bunches, a medium thick skin and is moderately vigorous in growth. Our trials highlighted some problems, fruits split when hanging too long on the vine, which means they lack good keeping quality. But I can assure you that when those fruits are ready to eat, nobody thinks of leaving them on the vines!

For real Labrusca flavour, try 'Concord' one of the most popular American cultivars. 'Concord Seedless' produces very small blue grapes. It is more of a curiosity but very suitable as a pie-grape.

In early September we harvest 'Suffolk Red', a bright, beautiful red, with medium-sized, sweet and fruity berries in medium to good-sized bunches. This cultivar is vigorous, productive and has healthy vines. Of the same harvesting period and colour is 'Canadice Seedless'. This is aromatic and has a soft texture and can be left on the vine for a month without problems. It is of medium vigour, good health, very productive but tends to overcrop. 'Vanessa Seedless' has dark red, medium-sized, crunchy, thin-skinned berries of sweet and refined flavour. All three have medium-sized, well-filled bunches.

Coming to the latter part of September we find 'Flame'. It has dark red, refreshingly sweet, very large shouldered bunches of medium-sized berries, some rather small, but all ripening at the same time. Another late September cropper is 'Reliance' with fine and large, pinkish-red berries of refined Labrusca flavour in compact bunches that may cause problems with bunch rot in rainy periods.

In October we get 'Lakemont', which has not only the same parentage as 'Himrod' and 'Interlaken', but the same refined flavour and rather small berries. Its small, long, good looking bunches will stand even a cold and wet autumn. A good reminder of the two earlier ones.

Later maturing, and rarely reliable as an outdoor grape is 'Thompson Seedless'. An excellent cultivar for raisins but also nicely flavoured, rather small berries in broad bunches. We grow 'Thompson Seedless' in a cold greenhouse where it succeeds in a normal summer ready for picking early October.

In the same ripening season but requiring less heat and producing dark blue berries is the old 'Black Monukka'. Both cultivars have oval berries in large bunches with refined flavour, if you can provide them with the necessary warmth; either an extremely protected wall or a cold greenhouse.

All thin-skinned cultivars are suitable for drying and for grape juice and, being seedless, they can also be used for cooking and baking in pies and desserts, although the thick-skinned cultivars are preferable for this.

Altogether seven years' experience in growing seedless grapes, about five of which were in handling actual fruits, is of course not very long, but the years ahead will bring more experience and more cultivars to compare. Those first years of trials have clearly shown that seedless grapes, spread over the many cultivars that exist, offer new perspectives for growing outdoor grapes in our climate. With each season and with each new cultivar we get to know more about these plants and hope that finally we can select those that offer new possibilities, new flavours and more enjoyment in growing seedless grapes outdoors and I sincerely hope to share my enthusiasm with many, many people.

PETER BAUWENS, nurseryman, lives in the village of De Klinge close to the Dutch province of Zeeland north-west of Antwerp. He is near enough the sea for the climate to be a maritime one but being on the Continent, it is a little colder in winter and warmer in summer than in south-east England. Having visited him three times, I would estimate that his season is about one to two weeks earlier than Britain.

HOWARD STRINGER

Grapes Gone to Pot

RAY WAITE

GRAPES GROWN AS STANDARDS make attractive pot plants and enable vines to be grown in a small space. In pots they are easy to move around allowing them to spend the winter under cover in a conservatory or cool greenhouse and then be stood outside during the summer months. And what could be more enjoyable than picking the sun-ripened fruit straight from the vine after an alfresco meal?

To grow grapes successfully in a container it pays to obtain a strong young rod (long growth produced in the current year); it is usual to buy pot-grown plants that are one or two years old. If the growth is less than pencil thickness cut it back at leaf-fall to one strong bud, often referred to as an eye. The resultant growth from this bud during the following year should be vigorous as it is essential to build up the main stem. Once this has been achieved prune the rod to a bud at a convenient height above the pot during the dormant season. The length of stem chosen will depend on the height of the greenhouse and the ease in which you feel you can manage to carry out work on the vine. If you vary the height of the vines it will also mean that you can group several together to save space.

The vine during the following year needs to be potted into a larger pot as soon as growth starts in the spring. A vine in a 13cm (5in) pot will need to move into a 19cm (7 1_2 in) pot but plants with larger root systems can be potted into a 23cm (9in) pot. It is far better to use a loam-based potting compost, John Innes No 3 for example, as this ensures that the plant is given stability. Standard vines will remain fruitful for up to seven to 10 years provided that they are potted on in spring ultimately into a pot size that is easy to move around. After this, top-dress with a potting compost in the spring to stimulate growth.

The fruiting head is built up in the first year. Keep the top four or five shoots and pinch at six leaves and remove any growths on the main stem completely. It is unlikely that flowers will appear but if they do remove them. They should not be allowed to develop into fruit at this stage or even over the next season as the fruitfulness of the vine can be impaired in future years.

In the second year prune the ripened shoots to one bud during the dormant season. This builds up short spurs to form the permanent head in just the same way as a standard rose or fuchsia is formed. To encourage well ripened shoots, stand the vine out-of-doors from early summer onwards, making sure that it is watered adequately and fed regularly with a proprietary general liquid fertilizer.

During the third year prune once again to one bud in early winter. It is quite possible that some fruit will be produced this time but allow only one or two bunches to mature. Pinch growths at two leaves beyond the bunch, or again at six leaves where no fruit has appeared. Support will be necessary for the growths, so loop them into a central strong bamboo cane. Give regular applications of a general liquid fertilizer up to the fruit set followed by a high potash feed such as tomato fertilizer.

VINES FOR TABLE DECORATION

At Wisley we have adopted a Victorian method for growing vines in pots and find that very acceptable fruiting specimens can be obtained. Two methods are used. The first makes slightly larger plants with up to six bunches depending on the cultivar. Before the vines start into growth choose one of the previous year's vigorous growths and pass the tip up through the hole of an 11cm (8in) clay pot. Fill the pot with John Innes No 3 potting compost and firm it, leaving a space for watering. It is necessary, of course, to rig up some support to hold the pot in an elevated position. Try building a stage using timber uprights to hold a small slotted platform or make a metal tripod to keep the pot in place.

The top of the stem should be no more than 60cm (24in) from its tip to the compost level which should provide for approximately four or five eyes. A short stout bamboo cane will keep the stem erect especially once the fruit has formed. Tie in the fruiting shoots as they can become quite heavy with the maturing grapes. Remove growths below the pot and pinch those above at two leaves beyond any bunch, then thin in the normal way as soon as the berries are about pea size. Once the fruit has ripened, gradually sever the stem from the parent plant and allow it to stand on its own root system, taking care to ensure that it does not dry out.

Growing vines for table decoration. The first method (below left) uses a single rod, passing the tip through the hole of an 11cm pot. A second method (below right) is by coiling the rod in the base of a pot or thirdly (bottom) by layering a length of the previous year's growth

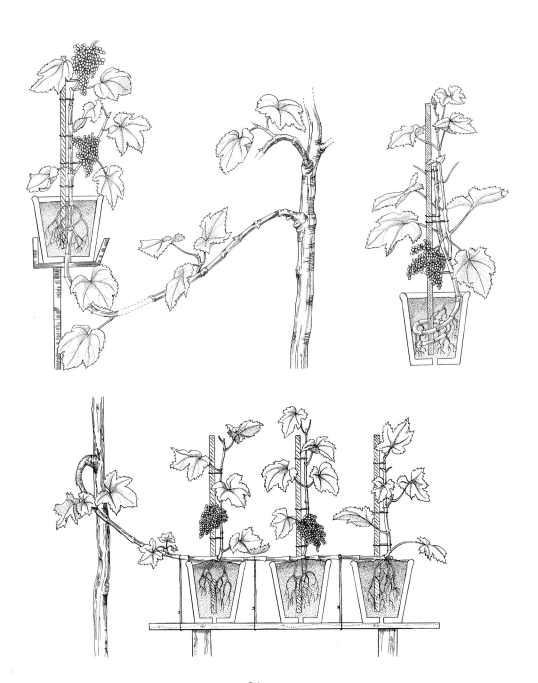

The other method of pot cultivation is to layer a whole length of the previous year's growth on to a 15cm (6in) pot. In Victorian times a young rod was pot grown then bent over so that it came in close contact with the compost that had been firmed in the pots prior to layering. As a compromise, select well ripened growths from the existing spur system of established rods and bend into position on pots supported on narrow staging below the vines. The layered stem forms roots below every eye which in turn grows upright and often carries one or more bunches; again pinch at two leaves beyond the bunch. Support the fruiting shoot with a cane and separate individual fruiting stems by cutting the layer either side of the pot when the grapes have ripened.

For both methods it is important to keep the pots well watered and fed with a high potash fertilizer during the growing season. At Wisley we have found 'Black Hamburgh', 'Buckland Sweetwater', 'Foster's Seedling', 'Mrs Pearson', 'Mrs Pince' and 'Muscat of Alexandria' successful using both methods.

Another method of producing grapes on small plants, which is simple to do but has a limited cropping propensity, is the use of coils. A 1 to 1.3m (3-4ft) length of the previous year's growth has the bottom 60cm (2ft) or so coiled round inside a 23cm (9in) pot which is then filled with John Innes Compost No 2 and evenly consolidated. Ideally place the prepared pot on bottom heat to accelerate root formation and subsequent growth. Insert a stout cane centrally to give vertical support to the remaining part of the stem.

In effect what has been achieved is really the rooting of a long hardwood cutting, and as with the previous methods this should be carried out in late winter or spring prior to the vine starting into growth.

RECOMMENDED CULTIVARS

'Black Hamburgh' still the most reliable black early Sweetwater grape available. Excellent for training in pots.

'Buckland Sweetwater' a good white grape which sets freely and is ideal for growing in pots. It is not vigorous so feed well.

'Foster's Seedling' an early Sweetwater type ripening early but soon losing flavour when fully ripe. Good in an unheated greenhouse.

'Mrs Pince' a strong growing Muscat type which ripens late and produces high quality grapes. Requires some warmth in late autumn to ripen well.

'Muscat of Alexandria' the finest flavoured grape but requires warmth at pollination time and to obtain really successful ripening. It can be difficult to set fruit and definitely requires hand pollination.

'Muscat Champion' does not keep in good quality for long but has excellent flavour as a mid season grape.

'Muscat Hamburgh' ripens earlier than most other Muscats. It can be difficult to grow well but is worth growing for its black highly flavoured fruits.

RAY WAITE, Superintendent of Glasshouses at the RHS Garden Wisley, is co-author of the Wisley Handbook Grapes Indoors and Out with Harry Baker and contributes to The Garden

Flavoursome Fruits

Harry Baker

THE STRAWBERRY is our favourite soft fruit and in 1993 we consumed 48,000 tons of home grown strawberries, not counting those grown in gardens. Some critics say that modern strawberries do not have the flavour of yesteryears nor do we have much choice. I think they are wrong on both counts. Thanks to the work of plant breeders on both sides of the Atlantic there is a greater number than ever before and the majority with good flavour. My choice for the garden, in season order, is 'Honeoye', very early; 'Hapil', mid; 'Symphony', mid; 'Tenira', mid to late and 'Aromel', a perpetual.

I must not forget to include a couple of golden oldies which have withstood the test of time – 'Royal Sovereign' and 'Cambridge Late Pine', the former was raised by Laxton Brothers and introduced in 1892 and the latter by Mr D Boyes of Cambridge in the 1950s. On the downside 'Royal Sovereign' is often only a moderate cropper, virus sensitive, degenerates quickly and is subject to mildew and botrytis as well. Indeed, some growers consider it to be outdated and overrated. 'Cambridge Late Pine' is also a moderate cropper but the sweetest of them all.

Remember always practise soil rotation and plant strawberries when the soil is warm, say July and August for good establishment and wilt avoidance.

Our heritage of good gooseberry cultivars comes mainly from the gooseberry clubs formed in the late 18th century. They were run by workers such as spinners, weavers and dyers and were principally in the North and Midlands. Annual competitions were nearly always held in the local hostelries and members competed to grow the heaviest gooseberry. Some of the prizes were unusual items such as copper kettles and bed warming pans; even a brace of pistols at one and a bag of soot at another.

Thanks to these clubs we have a wide choice of flavoursome cultivars you can eat straight from the plant. I recommend 'Whitesmith' and 'Langley Gage' with white fruit; 'Bedford Yellow' and 'Golden Drop', yellow; 'Early Green Hairy', green; 'Whinham's Industry' and 'Red Champagne', red. Another good white with a very sweet, rich flavour is called 'Thatcher', introduced in 1877 by a Mr Leicester. The only modern cultivar worthy of inclusion, cultivated not for its flavour, but for its strong resistance to American gooseberry mildew, is 'Invicta', a white kind for cooking.

Similarly with blackcurrants there are no modern cultivars that can honestly be described as flavoursome – with their complex parentage they seem to have lost the true blackcurrant taste. Contemporary cultivars have been bred for juice production, hardiness, compactness, disease resistance and heavy cropping. 'Ben Sarek' is the epitome of all these things, hence an excellent garden cultivar, but it needs plenty of sugar in cooking. Sweet old cultivars, large and luscious, are 'Boskoop Giant', 'Blacksmith' and 'Raven', also 'Baldwin' for its high vitamin C content but these too have their faults. They can suffer from mildew and leaf spot, are susceptible to spring frosts and, with the exception of 'Baldwin', are very vigorous.

Red- and whitecurrants are not as popular as their darker relative, which is a pity because they are much hardier, need less space and are just as or even more productive. They, like the gooseberry, crop on the old and young wood so are ideal for growing in space-saving forms such as the cordon and the fan. The seeds tend to be too dominant for pies but both make a lovely jelly, an attractive wine and redcurrants are an essential ingredient of a summer pudding. Two redcurrant cultivars recommended for flavour and with large succulent berries are the early 'Jonkheer van Tets' and the mid to late 'Stanza'. A good white is 'White Grape' and a pink is 'Champagne'.

Raspberries are one of my favourite soft fruits. They are excellent for dessert and preserves, freeze well, are highly productive and will grow successfully in full sun or part shade. Incidentally, raspberries for dessert are best served cool rather than straight from the plant. I discovered this at a fruit tasting at Wisley when, unintentionally, some were served at room temperature and some cold from a refrigerator. The cooler berries scored the highest marks, unlike strawberries which are best unchilled.

There are plenty of well flavoured raspberry cultivars and more are soon to be released from the Scottish Crop Research Institute and Horticulture Research International, East Malling. For the present I recommend 'Glen Moy', 'Glen Prosen', 'Admiral' and 'Leo', the latter particularly for jam making. Having said this my favourite for dessert is still the old cultivar 'Malling Jewel' even though the berries are relatively small; it is compact and neat, easy to pick and does not sucker like the others. A new one worth trying is 'Redsetter' which is very like 'Malling Jewel' in habit but with larger berries. Sadly the best flavoured of them all, 'Lloyd George', has almost disappeared.

Of the autumn raspberries there is nothing to compare with 'Autumn Bliss'. My only criticisms are that it suckers prolifically and, because it does not part easily from the centre plug, picking can be a little tedious.

The last of the soft fruits I will mention is the American highbush blueberry, a bigger and much more productive relative of the whortleberry or bilberry of British moorlands. It is a lovely fruit especially in pies and muffins. Cut open a hot blueberry pie and the perfume of roses will assail you. Strangely, even though it is a sweet fruit, it needs a lot of sugar in cooking to bring out its full flavour. The blueberry is extremely fussy about soil, which must be light, well drained and, most essentially, acid, ideally with a pH between 4.5 and 5.5. Neutral and alkaline soils are totally unsuitable. Good cultivars abound and I recommend 'Earliblue', 'Bluecrop' and 'Berkeley' for heavy cropping as well as flavour. They are not fully self-fertile so it is best to plant more than one cultivar.

TREE FRUITS

The apple is our favourite tree fruit and no other nation grows so many cultivars in its gardens. Our cool, temperate climate suits the apple as the sometimes rather delicate nuances of flavour and scent are not burnt off by the summer sun. 'Cox's Orange Pippin' for example, is but a pale shadow of its English self, when grown in California, where the fruits when picked soon become mealy and of short season.

Faced with such a vast choice what are my favourites? Space, or rather lack of, allows me to mention but a few. First on the list, above all others, is 'Captain Kidd', a highly coloured crimson sport of 'Kidd's Orange Red' from New Zealand, season November to January. 'Captain Kidd' is a fine textured fruit, crisp, sweet and aromatic with just a hint of Palma violet in its flavour. Next comes 'Cox's Orange Pippin' – too well known to warrant description – and then 'D'Arcy Spice' a late dessert apple for eating December to April. It is a rather scruffy looking russet which shrivels in storage but retains its lovely spicy flavour, as the name implies. 'D'Arcy Spice' is best peeled as the skin is rather tough. 'Pixie', or the sport 'Red Pixie', is an excellent garden apple staying hard, crisp and juicy throughout its season of December to March. The fruits, however, tend to be small unless rigorously thinned.

Another first class but small garden apple is 'Sunset' with a season of October to December. It is a seedling from 'Cox' with many of its virtues but none of its faults. Last but not least is 'Fortune', a late summer apple from September to October. Crisp, juicy, sweet and aromatic, 'Fortune' needs exposure to full sun to bring out its best flavour. Unfortunately, it tends to be biennial, bearing a heavy crop every other year. Other flavoursome apples I can only briefly mention are 'Ribston Pippin', 'Egremont Russet', 'King Russet', 'Falstaff', 'William Crump', 'Jupiter', 'Spartan', 'Orleans Reinette', 'Blenheim Orange' and 'Ashmead's Kernel'.

Pears in profusion are seldom seen in British gardens and the reasons are not hard to find. Pears flower early and hence are often spoilt by frosts; trees are slow to come into bearing and fruit can suffer badly from scab. They also need warmth and sun for the fruits to ripen properly. The three most commonly planted are 'Williams' Bon Chrétien', 'Conference' and 'Doyenné du Comice', all good pears, especially the latter which in my opinion is the finest in the world. I would also add 'Concorde' – a sort of up market 'Conference' – 'Merton Pride', 'Onward' and 'Olivier de Serres'. 'Merton Pride', is a large juicy pear with melting, creamy coloured flesh of intense flavour. 'Onward' can be best described as a summer 'Doyenné du Comice', fine textured and juicy. 'Olivier de Serres' is a winter pear – February to March - shaped like a small apple with white flesh and a very strong aromatic, musky flavour. Finally I must mention the Asiatic pear, *Pyrus serotina*, which is occasionally seen on sale in supermarkets as the Nashi pear. It is attractive, often apple shaped, with yellow skin overlaid with a fine golden russet. The flesh is crisp and juicy and it keeps well for a pear. However, compared with the European pear, it tastes rather insipid. Nevertheless the Asiatic pear makes a superb addition to a green salad, and that, I think, is where its true forte lies.

The true origin of the gage group of plums is lost in the mists of time but they are thought to have originated in Armenia. From there they spread to Greece and eventually throughout Europe and the Americas. Gages are sweeter than plums with a syrupy almost cloying flavour. They are usually small and yellow or green in colour but can have large pink or red fruits. All by definition are flavoursome, nevertheless some are better than others. My selection is 'Willingham Gage', a seedling from 'Cambridge Gage' but sweeter and richer, 'Old English Greengage', 'Royale de Vilvoorde', a luscious largish pink and grey fruit and firm-fleshed 'Jefferson' from the USA. Of the plums I select three: 'Reeves Seedling', 'Kirke's Blue' and 'Coe's Golden Drop'. All are delicious, but, like so many good things in life, they do not come easily. They are not self-fertile so cross pollination is necessary and they require a warm, sunny summer as well as a frost-free spring if they are to bear fruit.

With the advent of less vigorous rootstocks and self-fertile cultivars, sweet cherries are now a much more feasible proposition for the garden, although on good soils they can still grow to relatively large trees of up to $5\frac{1}{2}$ to 6m (18-20ft) in height and spread. I will mention only one – 'Stella', a self-fertile dark purple cherry with firm, almost crackly red flesh. 'Stella' was a worthy recipient of the RHS Award of Garden Merit in 1993. The best acid cherry is 'Morello'.

There is nothing quite like a fully ripe apricot eaten straight from the tree, far better than the under ripe hard fruits so often seen for sale in supermarkets and greengrocers. However, they are a temperamental fruit; among the earliest to flower and hence their cropping is erratic. They need a warm, sunny situation so are best grown against a wall in a fairly heavy chalky loam. They can become quite large trees so perhaps a better way of growing them is in a pot where the roots are contained. All available cultivars are good – I like 'Alfred', 'Farmingdale' and 'Moor Park'.

In Victorian times no head gardener worthy of his salt would serve his master with anything but the white-fleshed peaches and nectarines and I would agree. They are superior in every way to the yellow fleshed. The best outdoor peaches in this regard are 'Duke of York' and 'Peregrine' and the best nectarine is 'Lord Napier', though the latter needs the protection of glass to acquire its true flavour. The finest peach I have ever tasted is the China flat peach or Java peach, also known as the Pentao (Peen-to), *Prunus persica platycarpa*. However the flat peach flowers early, needs a good deal of warmth and is very prone to peach leaf curl. It is far better in a pot under glass at least until the dangers of frost and leaf curl are over.

The above reflects only my own personal opinion of flavoursome fruits. Nevertheless I hope I have written sufficient to whet the appetite and perhaps persuade more people to plant fruit.

HARRY BAKER, former Fruit Officer and Assistant Curator of the RHS Garden Wisley, is Vice Chairman of the RHS Fruit Group and a member of the Society's Fruit and Vegetable Committee.

Fruit Tree Rootstocks

TONY WEBSTER

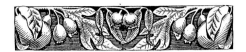

MOST FRUIT TREES grown in Britain are made up of two genetically distinct components. The scion comprises the upper part of the trunk and all other above-ground parts of the tree, and the second component is the rootstock, consisting of the root system and the lower part of the trunk. Occasionally, fruit trees may have a third component, the interstock, or interstem, which is grafted between the scion and rootstock as an intermediate section of the tree trunk.

Fruit trees do not come true to type from seed and so selected cultivars must be propagated vegetatively. They are rarely grown on their own roots on account of difficulties with their vegetative propagation from cuttings or layers. Although recent research has resolved some of these problems, the technique is still not easy and budding or grafting scions on to rootstocks remains the most commonly used method of fruit tree propagation.

While most prospective growers of fruit trees are likely to spend considerable time and effort choosing an appropriate scion, they usually give less consideration to the choice of rootstock or interstock. Indeed, when they buy trees many gardeners are completely unaware of the rootstock's existence. This is unfortunate, as rootstocks and interstocks offer much more to the horticulturist than just a means of propagating the scion. Often they will determine the vigour and eventual size of the tree and can help adapt it to particular soil or site conditions. They may, for instance, provide resistance or tolerance to troublesome soil-borne pests and diseases or enable the tree to survive in droughty soils or those with seasonal drainage problems. By choosing the appropriate rootstock the fruit grower can also influence how soon the tree comes into cropping after planting, its yield, productivity and the quality of the fruits produced.

Taking account of these valuable attributes, it is essential to give due consideration to the choice of rootstock when buying the tree.

HISTORY AND DEVELOPMENT OF ROOTSTOCK USE

Traditionally, all rootstocks were raised from seed, using seed extracted from fruits collected from indigenous wild populations of pip and stone fruits. Usually, the seedling rootstocks and the fruiting clones grafted on them were of the same botanical species. Use of such rootstocks is thought to go back more than 2,000 years and they are known to have been employed by horticulturists in ancient Greek civilization.

Sources of seed were readily available and the seedlings were generally well adapted to local conditions. The early horticulturists soon mastered the techniques for breaking seed dormancy and the skills of grafting the scion to the rootstock.

The timing of the first use of clonal (vegetatively propagated) rootstocks is uncertain, although records suggest that they have been used in apple culture since the 17th century. It is also not clear whether the adoption of clonal rootstocks was in response to the need for greater uniformity of performance or to the need to control the vigour of the scion. Some of the early selections of clonal rootstocks were propagated from suckers dug up from around the base of existing trees. Indeed, the plum rootstock 'Pershore', popular in the West Midlands plum growing region, was propagated in this manner until only 25 years ago. Without doubt the most important criterion in the early selection of clonal rootstocks was their ease of propagation. However, in the last 70 years many other attributes have assumed equal if not greater importance. These include scion vigour control, resistance to soil-borne diseases and pests and the tendency of young trees to come early into their first fruiting and produce an abundant crop.

Fruit trees rootstocks are propagated either sexually (that is, from seeds) or asexually (vegetatively) from layers, stools, stem or root cuttings or by tissue culture (micropropagation). Both sexual and asexual methods of propagation are employed by nurserymen.

ROOTSTOCKS RAISED FROM SEED

Although all the rootstocks used for raising fruit trees in Britain are now of clonal origin, seedling-raised rootstocks are still widely used in raising selected clones of ornamental tree species such as *Sorbus* and *Crataegus*. Moreover, in many other fruit-growing areas of the world seedling rootstocks still predominate and most of the world's peaches, nectarines, plums and apricots are grown on trees propagated on seedling-raised rootstocks. These have three clear advantages over their clonally raised counterparts:

They are generally much cheaper to grow.

Less sophisticated nursery equipment is required for their propagation.

Their use may carry less risk of virus transfer to the scion, as many viruses of pip fruit are not seedling transmitted. This is not true with stone fruits such as cherries, however, where viruses are seedling transmitted.

Unfortunately, with the exception of some apomictic (where fruits are produced without fertilization) types of rootstock used in citrus culture, most seedling rootstocks are variable in their growth and in the characteristics they confer to the scion.

To reduce the variability associated with seedling rootstocks fruit breeders and horticulturists have attempted to produce virus-free lines of seedlings with improved uniformity (homogeneity) which also have other beneficial effects upon scion growth. This work continues up to the present day and many improved seedling-raised rootstocks for stone fruits have been developed in recent years. Examples are the mazzard (*Prunus avium*) rootstocks 'Pontavium' and 'Pontaris', developed by the National Institute for Agricultural Research (INRA) in France. These two clones are cross compatible and when planted together as virus-free trees in isolated 'mother tree' orchards, produce abundant crops of healthy seeds for use in raising rootstocks. Similar improved rootstocks for other stone fruits such as plum (prune), apricot and peach have also been produced in France, usually by hybridizations between two or more *Prunus* species. Most of these are propagated sexually, that is, from seeds.

Where vigour control in the scion is desired seedling rootstocks are usually found wanting. Trees on most seedling stocks are extremely vigorous and slow to come into bearing. Only with crops such as peaches, where these factors are of less importance, or with mechanically harvested crops where dwarf tree size is a disadvantage, have seedling rootstocks retained their primacy.

CLONAL ROOTSTOCKS

An increasing proportion of the apple, pear and cherry trees raised worldwide are grown on clonal rootstocks and all rootstocks used for fruit trees in Britain are of clonal origin. Almost all size-controlling rootstocks, that is the dwarfing or semi-dwarfing types, are clonal.

All clonal rootstocks are raised vegetatively from layers (stools), cuttings or by *in vitro* micropropagation. The advantages over seedling rootstocks are that they produce scion trees of much more uniform growth and cropping, facilitate the control of scion vigour and branching habit, provide resistance to soil-borne pests and diseases, and can be selected for their adaptability on different soil types.

Vegetative propagation is, however, more expensive and requires more skill than seed propagation and this has prevented its adoption in many parts of the world. Nevertheless, the breeding and selection of clonal rootstocks has been the major influence in the progress of fruit growing in the United Kingdom during the last 25 years.

INTERSTOCKS

Occasionally referred to as interstems, interstocks form an intermediate part of the trunk between the scion and the rootstock. For many years their principal use in Britain was for overcoming graft incompatibility between pear varieties, such as 'Williams' Bon Chrétien', and quince rootstocks. Other pear cultivars, such as 'Beurré Hardy', were used as interstocks to alleviate this incompatibility.

Interstocks for apple may be formed from either rootstocks or from other scion cultivars. Dwarfing rootstocks, such as M9 or M27, are used as interstocks in raising apple trees, where soil conditions are not suited to planting trees with the dwarfing clone itself used as the rootstock. In these instances, more vigorous clones, such as MM106 or MM111, are used. Vigour of such trees usually falls between that of the rootstock and of the interstock when used alone. Another reason for using interstocks is when a dwarfing rootstock is itself very difficult to propagate.

Unfortunately, dwarfing rootstock clones for plum and sweet cherry usually show little ability to dwarf scions when used as interstocks and are rarely used when raising stone fruit trees.

Often an interstock is formed from another apple scion variety. In central and eastern Europe, where winter temperatures are more severe than in Britain, interstocks of cold-tolerant apple cultivars such as 'Hibernal' are still regularly used by commercial growers. In Holland, apple scion cultivars such as 'Zoete Aagt' and 'Golden Delicious' are sometimes recommended as interstocks and are reported to increase cropping precocity on young trees.

CLONAL ROOTSTOCKS FOR APPLE

Almost all rootstocks now used for raising apples in Europe and an increasing proportion of those used in the USA are propagated clonally. Unlike pears and many of the stone fruit species, which may be grafted on to a range of different genera and species, apples are almost always raised on selections of the apple species itself, *Malus domestica.*

The First East Malling Selections

By the turn of the 19th century many of the apple clonal rootstocks used in Britain and other parts of northern Europe had become mixed and were frequently incorrectly named. To rectify this situation, selection work was begun by Wellington and completed by Hatton, successive directors of East Malling Research Station between 1913 and 1949. As many as possible of the clonal rootstocks then available for apple were obtained from nurseries in Britain and on the Continent; these were then sorted and classified on the basis of their morphological characteristics. As the names under which they had been obtained were confused and inaccurate, it was decided to give each distinct clone a new and incontestable identification. The first nine distinct clones were therefore designated Type I

through to Type IX (see Table 1); the word Malling was subsequently substituted for Type.

Hatton and his co-workers later acquired further apple rootstock clones, principally from Germany. These, all of which were very vigorous when budded with scions, were characterised and given the designation Malling X through to Malling XVI.

Of these early selections only Malling VII and Malling IX (now referred to as M7 and M9) remain of commercial interest. M7 was, until recently, the most popular clonal rootstock in the USA, mainly on account of its intermediate vigour, adaptability to different soil types, ease of propagation and tolerance to winter cold. More recently, the trend towards closer plantings, using dwarfed trees, has seen M7 lose some of its supremacy in the USA. In most other parts of the world it has been superseded by MM106, which generally suckers less and induces more productive cropping.

M9, in contrast, remains the most important dwarfing rootstock used for apple in most countries of the world. Over the last 30 years its popularity has greatly increased with the move towards closer plantings of dwarfed trees. Its principal merits lie in its dwarfing effect upon the scion, its promotion of precocious and consistent cropping, its production of large fruits and its resistance to collar rot, *Phytophthora cactorum.*

Unfortunately it has some disadvantages. It is more difficult to propagate than most other apple rootstocks and has brittle roots. This means that scion trees grafted on M9 are insecurely anchored unless supported by a stout stake. In some other parts of the world

Table 1: The original nine Paradise (Malling) apple rootstocks			
Type No	**Previous common name**	**Current Malling clone number**	**Vigour**
I	Broad-leaved English Paradise	M1	Vigorous
II	Doucin	M2	Vigorous
III	(no name)	M3	Semi-dwarf
IV	Holstein Doucin	M4	Intermediate
V	Doucin Améliore	M5	Vigorous
VI	River's Nonsuch Paradise	M6	Very vigorous
VII	(no name)	M7	Semi-dwarf
VIII	French Paradise (Clark Dwarf)	M8	Dwarf
IX	Paradise Jaune de Metz	M9	Dwarf

its sensitivity to drought, winter cold injury and fireblight damage have also prevented its widespread use.

In recent years attempts have been made to overcome the poor propagation of M9 by selecting improved clones. Work by nurserymen and researchers in Belgium, France and Germany has produced selections which are easier to propagate on the layer bed than the East Malling Long Ashton Scheme, EMLA, (virus free) selection of M9 (Table 2). Most of these selections originated as sports found in existing nursery stool beds, but research at East Malling has shown that similar easily propagated clones of M9 can be produced by repeated subculturing of the EMLA M9 clone in micropropagation.

Amateur fruit growers thinking of using M9 rootstock should be aware that the trees will need firm support and that they will grow poorly unless planted on fertile, deep loams and kept free of competition from weeds or grass. Where these criteria cannot be met, alternative, more invigorating rootstocks should be chosen. Another choice is to acquire trees on stronger rootstocks, such as MM106 or MM111, but with interstocks of M9. Such trees are usually of intermediate vigour, but more tolerant of poorer soils and slight neglect than those worked directly on M9 rootstocks.

Table 2: New selections of M9 rootstock made in Europe		
Selection name/number	**Origin**	**Vigour compared to M9 EMLA**
Pajam 1	France	Slightly less
Pajam 2	France	Similar
Nicolai 29	Belgium	Slightly more

The Merton and Malling Merton selections

Soon after the original Malling selections were made by Hatton and his co-workers, researchers in Britain recognised that some of these rootstocks had serious shortcomings. The best way of improving the range of rootstocks available was to breed new ones. One of the prime objectives of the early breeding work was resistance to the woolly apple aphid, *Eriosoma lanigerum*. In many apple-producing regions of the world, especially those with hotter climatic conditions than Britain such as Australia, New Zealand and South Africa, woolly apple aphid causes severe damage to rootstock roots. One of the best sources of resistance to this pest is the apple scion cultivar 'Northern Spy'. In a programme of work at the John Innes Institute, then based at Merton in England, 'Northern Spy' was crossed with M2, producing a new rootstock, Merton 793, which showed strong resistance to woolly apple aphid damage. Merton 793 is still widely used in South Africa and parts of New Zealand, but its strong vigour on all but the poorest soils makes it ill-suited to the more intensive plantings and smaller trees favoured by many fruit growers in the last 25 years.

Further crosses using 'Northern Spy' as one parent were then carried out in a joint programme of work between East Malling Research Station and the John Innes Institute. It was from this programme that the Malling Merton (MM) series of rootstocks emerged, all of which exhibit resistance to woolly apple aphid attacks to the roots of the trees. Although 15 Malling Merton selections were made initially and distributed for trials throughout the world, only four were planted in any quantity (Table 3). Two of these, MM104 and MM109, both very vigorous rootstocks, have since fallen from favour with growers because of their susceptibility to collar rot and poor anchorage.

MM106 remains one of the most popular rootstocks worldwide. It has been planted extensively in New Zealand, South America, Australia, and the USA, as well as in many parts of Europe. It is a semi-vigorous rootstock on highly fertile soils but produces trees of intermediate stature on poorer soils. MM106 is very easy to propagate, either by stooling or cutting techniques, and trees on it crop precociously and show high productivity. The main disadvantage is its sensitivity to collar rot, which can be particularly damaging to trees planted on heavy clay soils with poor drainage which favour this fungus. Also, trees on MM106 tend to produce slightly smaller fruit than those grafted on M9 and this can prove a problem with small-fruited scion varieties.

Table 3: Popular Malling Merton rootstock clones		
Clone Number	**Parentage**	**Vigour**
MM104	M2 x 'Northern Spy'	Vigorous
MM106	'Northern Spy' x M1	Intermediate
MM109	M2 x 'Northern Spy'	Vigorous
MM111	'Northern Spy' x Merton 793	Vigorous

Although often of little consequence to the home gardener, slightly smaller fruit size can tilt the balance from profit to loss for many commercial producers.

MM106 is an excellent rootstock for the gardener seeking a medium-sized tree which will tolerate some competition from weeds, grass and other plants for water and nutrients.

MM111 produces trees which are slightly more vigorous than those on MM106 and has therefore proved less popular with modern commercial producers. Nevertheless, it performs well in droughty conditions and if trees on it are pruned and trained correctly they can prove very productive. Although still used in the United Kingdom by some 'Bramley's Seedling' producers, it is now mainly used on poorer soils in other parts of the world or as the under-stock in many trees with dwarfing inter-stocks.

Occasionally, trees may be offered on M25 rootstock. This originated from the same breeding programme as the Malling Merton Series ('Northern Spy' x M2) but as it did not inherit the desired resistance to woolly apple aphid it was not given an MM prefix. It is a very vigorous rootstock and has the unusual merit for a rootstock in this vigour category of inducing precocious and productive cropping in the scion. In Britain and other countries where root attacks of woolly aphid are not a problem, M25 has an appeal for those seeking traditional standard-sized apple trees.

Despite the considerable success of the Malling Merton series of rootstocks in counteracting the worst effects of woolly apple aphid damage, it is of some concern that there is evidence of this resistance breaking down in some areas of the world. Future rootstock breeding programmes may need to look for new sources of resistance to this troublesome fruit pest.

Other Malling apple rootstock selections

In parallel with breeding for woolly apple aphid resistance, in the 1920s fruit breeders at East Malling Research Station began attempts to extend the vigour range of apple rootstocks. At that time only two dwarfing stocks were known, M9 and the poorly performing M8. The former was used as one parent in a series of crosses and after extensive screening and orchard testing over a period of more than 30 years, two new rootstock clones were selected, M26 and M27.

Trees on M26 (M16 x M9) are semi-dwarf, intermediate in vigour between those on M9 and on MM106. Although an excellent rootstock for 'Bramley's Seedling', M26 has proved less successful with 'Cox's Orange Pippin' and its various clones. M26 has proved popular with producers in both North and South America, where its tolerance of low winter temperatures and ease of propagation have proved particularly attractive. Unfortunately, M26 frequently produces many burr knots on the above-ground rootstock trunk (shank) and in some parts of the world these provide easy access to pests and diseases. Also, the vascular system in the M26 shank often develops irregularly, producing trunks with a fluted appearance. These shank abnormalities often lead to stunted or variable growth in the scion. The best way of overcoming this is to plant trees on M26 with their unions as close as possible to, but not actually touching, the soil surface. Despite its disadvantages M26 is often the best rootstock to use when growing trees in large tubs or other containers.

M27 (M13 x M9) was the first fully dwarfing apple rootstock made widely available to commerce. If trees on M27 are to grow well and remain productive they must be planted on deep fertile loam soils, maintained free from weeds and grass, irrigated when soil moisture levels are depleted and pruned annually to sustain a balance of new growth and fruiting spurs. Without this care and attention trees on M27 tend to become stunted and stop producing new extension growth after only a few years so that the spurs become progressively less productive and fruit size diminishes. Commercially, M27 is now only recommended for use with naturally vigorous scion cultivars, such as 'Bramley's Seedling' and 'Jonagold', and planted on the most fertile and moisture-retentive soils. Although often offered to the gardener as a fully dwarfing rootstock suitable for growing a tree on the patio, it should be borne in mind that such trees will need regular watering, weeding and feeding if they are to thrive.

Apple rootstock breeding and selection is continuing at East Malling (now known as Horticulture Research International [HRI] – East Malling) and the current goals are to expand the vigour range and to develop rootstocks which have none of the shortcomings of the existing rootstocks mentioned above. More than 100 different apple rootstock clones are currently under examination in screening trials at East Malling and several of the more promising of these have recently been distributed for further testing in Europe and New Zealand. The most advanced selection is AR.86-1-20, which produces trees of similar or slightly less vigour than those on MM106 and induces similar cropping performance in the scion. Its special attribute is an apparent greater resistance to collar rot. This rootstock is performing particularly well in a preliminary trial on a poor soil in New Zealand.

Future breeding goals will continue to be the production of dwarfing stocks which show better anchorage, resistance to woolly apple aphid and the promotion of large-sized fruit. Possible limitations on the use of herbicides in the future and limitations on water supplies in the south-east of Britain may suggest that a new goal for fruit breeders should be dwarfing apple rootstocks that are more drought-tolerant.

Apple rootstocks from other parts of the world

Although most of the apple clonal rootstocks used throughout the world over the last 70 years have been those either selected or bred at East Malling, it is perhaps inevitable that they have not proved suitable in all situations. They were, after all, selected with British conditions in mind. Some apple-producing areas suffer problems not experienced in the United Kingdom and apple rootstock breeding programmes in these areas have focused on alleviating these difficulties.

One of the major objectives has been to select dwarfing rootstocks, with vigour between that of M27 and M26 which have much greater resistance to injury from winter cold than the sensitive M9. In many parts of central Europe and North America very low winter tem-

Table 4: New dwarfing rootstock clones produced by European and USA fruit breeders

Country of origin	Rootstock series or name	Promising clones	Rootstock attributes
Poland	P Series	P1, P2, P16, and P22	Resistance to winter cold injury – dwarfing – productive
Russia	Budagovski Series	Bud 9	Resistance to winter cold injury
Czech Republik	J-TE Series	Clones E, F, G, and H	Dwarfing and productive
USA	C G Series	Geneva 65	Resistance to fireblight, collar rot, and winter cold
Canada	Ottawa Series	Ottawa 3	Resistance to winter cold injury, good productivity

peratures frequently cause severe damage or even the death of trees grafted on M9. Rootstock breeding programmes in Poland, Russia, Canada, Sweden and Germany have all made winter cold tolerance one of their chief priorities.

Another objective has been to produce a fully dwarfing rootstock with resistance to woolly apple aphid. All the Malling Merton series are rather too vigorous for the currently popular intensive planting systems and this has somewhat curtailed development of such systems in parts of the southern hemisphere and elsewhere. Recent selections made at the Geneva Experimental Station in New York State, USA, may go some way to satisfying this need.

In parts of the eastern United States fireblight, *Erwinia amylovora*, is a serious disease of apples. Research has shown that M9 rootstocks are particularly sensitive to the disease in these areas. Research, again at Geneva, New York State, has therefore focused on selecting apple rootstocks with strong resistance to fireblight.

Table 4 shows some of the cold-tolerant and other rootstocks recently produced and their origin.

Lately, interest has developed in growing temperate fruits, chiefly apples, in dry arid and sub-tropical zones. This will inevitably lead to new demands on rootstock breeders for greater drought tolerance, low winter chilling requirement, and adaptability to the different soil types. Already there are requests from countries in South America for rootstocks with tolerance to winter chilling and soils with a low pH.

Not only is HRI, East Malling, testing many of the rootstocks bred abroad for their suitability for United Kingdom growing conditions, but it also takes account of the possible international value of its own new rootstocks.

CLONAL ROOTSTOCKS FOR PEARS

All pear trees grown in the United Kingdom for fruit production are produced on clonal quince, *Cydonia oblonga*, rootstocks. In many other parts of the world, where the pear cultivars grown are incompatible with quince or where climatic and/or soil conditions do not favour the use of quince rootstocks, seedling-raised *Pyrus* rootstocks are commonly used for pear propagation. The species generally employed are *Pyrus communis* (the common pear), *P. betulifolia*, *P. calleryana* and *P. ussuriensis*. In countries where the Asian or Chinese pear (*P. pyrifolia*) cultivars are grown seedlings of this species, which is sometimes known as the sand pear, are often used as rootstocks.

The common pear is unusual in that it exhibits graft compatibility with species of several other Rosaceous genera such as *Amelanchier*, *Crataegus*, *Cotoneaster* and *Sorbus*, as well as compatibility with a few apple cultivars such as 'Winter Banana'. Sensitivity to fireblight by many of these species and poor growth and productivity of pear trees worked upon them has usually precluded their use as pear rootstocks.

Clonal selections of quince

Quince rootstocks are popular with pear growers on account of their beneficial effects upon pear scion growth and cropping. Generally, trees on quince stocks are less vigorous, crop more precociously and productively and bear fruit of larger size than trees grafted on *Pyrus* rootstocks. Moreover, quinces are also very much easier to propagate vegetatively than *Pyrus*. Nevertheless, they do have serious shortcomings. Many pear cultivars are graft-incompatible with quince (for example, 'Williams' Bon Chrétien' and 'Beurré Bosc') and an interstock of another cultivar such as 'Beurré Hardy' is needed to overcome this problem. Many quinces are also poorly anchored and trees require staking, particularly in their formative years. Not a problem in the United Kingdom but of serious concern in many other pear-growing regions of the world is their poor tolerance to low winter temperatures and their sensitivity to lime-induced chlorosis when planted on highly alkaline soils.

Two of the earliest clonal selections of quince were made at East Malling in the 1920s. These were Quince A and Quince C, two of five distinct types identified from 14 supposedly different quince clones collected by Ronald Hatton from British and Continental nurseries in 1914. Quince C is the more dwarfing of the two and is the choice of most commercial pear producers wishing to plant pears in single or multi-row

Table 5: Selections of quince rootstock used in continental Europe			
Quince selection	Origin	Vigour	Remarks
BA29	France (1966)	10 to 20% more vigorous than QA	The most popular quince rootstock in many parts of the world
Adams 332	Belgium (1965)	10 to 20% greater than QC	Three other Adams selections are also grown : C143 (Vaas) C145 (Guilliams) and the Pleurer (Hang) type.
Sydo	France (1975)	Similar to QA	Reported to perform better than QA in the nursery

Table 6: Clones of *Pyrus communis* used as rootstocks			
Pyrus clone	**Origin**	**Vigour**	**Remarks**
OHF333 (Brokmal)	USA (1960) from a cross between 'Old Home' and 'Farmingdale'	Similar or greater than BA29	Good performance on sandy soils in hot climates. Many other OHF types used in the USA
BP–1 (B13)	South Africa	Greater than QA	Difficult to propagate. Two other BP selections, numbers 2 and 3, are more invigorating as rootstocks
Brossier Series	France - selections from seedlings of Perry pears	Full range from RV139 which is very weak to RV113 which is very strong	Have proved extremely difficult to propagate

intensive systems of cultivation. Where larger trees are desired, or where soils are poorer or the scion cultivar is of weaker vigour, the slightly less dwarfing Quince A may be preferred.

In other pear-growing areas of the world different selections of quince rootstock are used and these are listed in Table 5.

Breeding and selection of quince rootstocks continues, with the aim of developing clones which are more dwarfing or which exhibit other improvements. Italian researchers have produced two clones, CTS 212 and CTS 214, both of which are between QA and QC in vigour, but are reputed to show greater tolerance to alkaline soil conditions. A new quince rootstock selection from the East Malling breeding programme is QR.193/16. It produces trees with similar or slightly greater vigour than QC but which bear fruits of larger size. Selections more dwarfing than Quince C are also currently under test in the East Malling programme.

Pyrus selections

In pear-growing regions where, because of severe winter cold, droughty or highly alkaline soils, quince rootstocks cannot be used, the pear grower must resort to using *Pyrus* rootstocks. Until recently there has been no interest in the use of *Pyrus* stocks in the United Kingdom. However, the high sensitivity of the cultivar 'Conference' to the mycoplasma that causes pear decline (Parry's disease) when budded on quince rootstocks has prompted the search for alternatives. The disease seems to cause a degeneration of the conducting tissues in the graft union between 'Conference' and quince rootstocks which may, in severe cases, lead to the death of the tree. It is hoped that selected *Pyrus communis* rootstock clones may show less sensitivity to this disease.

The principal problem in selecting clonal *Pyrus* rootstocks is that they tend to be extremely difficult to propagate vegetatively. All species, including *Pyrus communis*, the fruiting pear species itself, can be propagated from cuttings or layers only with extreme difficulty. Nevertheless, some clonal selections have been made and are listed in Table 6.

Clonal *Pyrus* rootstocks are also

being produced by fruit breeders in Italy, Germany and at East Malling. One series of rootstocks, produced by Dr Frank Alston at East Malling from a cross between BP1 and 'Old Home', is showing early promise in screening trials. New selections, from seedlings of the cultivars 'Old Home', 'Kirschensaller' and 'Beurré Hardy' are also under test and showing promise as rootstocks in France.

CLONAL ROOTSTOCKS FOR PLUMS

Thirty years ago a fruit nurseryman's catalogue in Britain would have listed plum trees for sale on an extensive range of rootstocks. 'Myrobalan B' (*Prunus cerasifera*), 'Brompton' (*P. domestica*), 'Marianna' (*P. cerasifera* x *P. munsoniana*), common plum (*P. domestica*), 'Damas C' (*P. domestica*), 'Pershore' (*P. domestica*) and 'St Julien A' (*P. insititia*) were all frequently used as rootstocks for plums, gages and damsons. Today, only one of these, the semi-dwarfing 'St Julien A' is in common use, although smaller quantities of 'Myrobalan B' and 'Brompton' are used for ornamental plum propagation. Difficulties with vegetative propagation have reduced the use of 'Pershore', which is a semi-dwarfing rootstock previously much favoured in the West Midlands. All the other rootstocks previously used are semi-vigorous or vigorous types and, for this reason,are of little interest to modern producers of plums.

In the early 1970s East Malling released a new selection of the St Julien type which was named 'Pixy'. Trees on 'Pixy' are 20 to 40 per cent less vigorous than trees on 'St Julien A' and crop more precociously, making them well suited for use in small gardens or in high-density commercial plantings. Nurserymen experienced difficulties in propagating 'Pixy' when it was first released and this has limited its adoption by commercial growers. Another problem with trees on 'Pixy' is that they produce small fruit. Unless the trees are well supplied with water and excess fruit is thinned, the fruit may prove too small for acceptance by the commercial markets. However, trees on 'Pixy' seem to show much less incidence of silver leaf disease than trees on 'St Julien A' and where large fruit size is not the priority, this rootstock deserves far more widespread use.

French researchers at Bordeaux have recently developed several new rootstocks suitable for plums and prunes. 'Victoria', grown in Holland and at East Malling on one of these, 'Ferlenain', produced trees slightly smaller than those on 'Pixy' with similar yield productivity and much better fruit size. Further trials will be needed, testing 'Ferlenain's graft compatibility with a range of plum cultivars before this new rootstock can be recommended for more extensive use in the United Kingdom. Another French rootstock clone, 'Ferciana/Ishtara' is also worthy of consideration. It produces trees similar in size to those on 'St Julian A' but with better fruit size.

New selections of 'Marianna'-type rootstocks selected in South Africa for use with Japanese-type plums (*Prunus salicina*) may also warrant consideration in the future in Britain. One of these, 'Maridon', proved compatible with 'Victoria' at East Malling and produced high-cropping trees of similar vigour to those on 'Pixy'. Unfortunately, suckering was a slight problem with this rootstock, as it is with most 'Marianna' types.

Until new rootstocks such as 'Ferlenain' and 'Maridon' are more fully tested, the amateur wishing to plant a small plum tree in the garden is advised to select 'Pixy' as the rootstock.

CLONAL ROOTSTOCKS FOR CHERRY

Sweet (*Prunus avium*) and sour (*P. cerasus*) cherries were traditionally produced on Mazzard (*P. avium*) seedling rootstocks in Britain. It was not until East Malling selected the clonal Mazzard type F12/1 that vegetative propagation of rootstocks began to become more popular for cherries. Nevertheless, a very large proportion of sweet and sour cherries grown worldwide are still propagated using seedling rootstocks. Most of these are of the Mazzard type, although where trees are grown on freely draining, gravelly soils, as in many parts of central and eastern Europe and the USA, seedlings of the Mahaleb (*Prunus mahaleb*, the perfumed cherry) may be preferred. A clonal selection of the Mahaleb type, 'St Lucie 64', was made many years ago in France, where it has become one of the most popular rootstocks for sweet and sour cherries grown on sandy, free-draining soils.

Where sweet or sour cherries are grown on soils with rather poor drainage, clonal selections of the sour cherry (*P. cerasus*) species are usually preferable as rootstocks.

Initially, sweet cherry rootstock breeding in Britain concentrated on resistance to the most damaging disease bacterial canker, *Pseudomonas* species. One Mazzard selection, 'Charger', released some years ago, shows improved resistance to bacterial canker and induces better scion cropping than F12/1.

Although most Morello-type sour cherries are relatively compact in habit, producing trees of small stature, almost all sweet cherry cultivars are very vigorous, producing very large trees unsuited to modern systems of commercial tree management or use in the small garden. Dwarfing rootstocks are needed to control their size. Unfortunately, breeding has failed to produce either Mazzard or Mahaleb rootstocks which can be used to reduce this inherent strong vigour of sweet cherry trees. Genetic dwarf types of Mazzard, raised by the John Innes Institute, although dwarfing, were extremely difficult to propagate vegetatively and produced very unproductive scion trees. To satisfy the demand for dwarfing rootstocks for sweet cherry, researchers have been forced to examine many other *Prunus* species and hybrids as potential rootstocks.

Although clones of *Prunus mugus*, *P. incisa*, *P. x dawyckensis* and *P. fruticosa* have been shown to dwarf sweet cherry trees very effectively, all of these have exhibited serious defects. *Prunus mugus* is very difficult to propagate, *P. incisa* produces poorly anchored trees often with small fruit size, trees on *P. x dawyckensis* crop poorly and *P. fruticosa*, which is also difficult to propagate, produces trees which sucker profusely.

More recently, clones of *P. cerasus* have shown considerable promise of providing dwarfing rootstocks for the sweet cherry. Trials in France indicate that one selection, 'Edabriz/Tabel', is particularly promising. Trees grafted on it are fully dwarfed and highly productive. Other selections of *P. cerasus*, the

'Weiroot' clones developed at Munich in Germany, also show promise although incompatibility with some sweet cherry scion cultivars has been reported.

Many fruit breeders believe that satisfactory dwarfing rootstocks for sweet cherry will only be produced by using hybrid rootstocks. One such hybrid, 'Colt', the result of a cross between *P. avium* and *P. pseudocerasus*, was released by East Malling in the 1970s. It is very easy to propagate and produces well-branched trees in the nursery. Although 'Colt' gives some reduction in scion size, the trees are still too vigorous for intensive planting systems. Nevertheless, trees on 'Colt' crop precociously and abundantly and bear large-sized fruits. It is also an excellent rootstock for Morello and Amarelle types of sour cherry.

The Belgian rootstock 'Inmil' is also of hybrid origin (*P. incisa* x *P. serrula*) and produces very dwarfed sweet cherry trees. Unfortunately, like 'Damil', another Belgian-bred rootstock (*P.* x *dawyckensis*), trees on 'Inmil' are relatively unproductive and may bear small-sized fruits.

Many new hybrid rootstocks, bred at Giessen in Germany, are currently under trial in several parts of the world and it is hoped that one or more of these may prove to be the fully dwarfing and productive rootstock long sought by sweet cherry producers.

Although rootstocks have been used for more than 2,000 years and rootstock research have been conducted for more than a century, how rootstocks bring about their many effects upon the scion remains largely an enigma. Nevertheless, breeding and selection has brought about considerable improvements in the choice of rootstocks available to both commercial and amateur fruit growers. Rootstocks still represent one of the least expensive, but most environmentally friendly, methods of controlling scion growth and cropping. It will be essential to continue breeding new rootstocks and testing them in integrated trials throughout the world if future needs, such as those stimulated by reductions in the use of agrochemicals and changes in the methods of orchard management, are to continue to be satisfied.

DR TONY WEBSTER is a member of the Perennial Crops Department, Horticultural Research International, East Malling.

Cordon Plums
for the Small Garden

GERALD EDWARDS

MANY GARDENERS wishing to cultivate fruit grow their apples and pears as cordons, yet are told by the gardening press that stone fruits must either be grown as fans or as bushes of some type. But I would suggest that plums and gages may be grown relatively easily and productively as cordons and that this method of growing is perhaps the best way for the gardener with the small garden. In referring to plums, I also include gages.

In the early 1980s, when I was undertaking a considerable amount of planting of apples and pears, I decided to plant a number of plum trees. However, as all my apples and pears were cordons, it would prove difficult to incorporate bush trees and in any case these trees would take up a considerable amount of space, and therefore I started thinking of planting the plums as cordons. I was aware that the French in the 18th and 19th centuries had experimented with many forms of fruit tree growing (and typical examples can be seen in the Hatton Fruit Garden at Bradbourne House, East Malling) and delving into various text books, I discovered that plums were among those fruits they experimented with. In those days they must have grown their fruit on

fairly vigorous rootstocks and this must have made life very difficult when dealing with trained fruit trees. I therefore figured that with the dwarfing rootstock 'Pixy', the growing of plums as cordons *should* be a relatively easy task.

While undertaking my research I was interested to note that Bonham Bazeley, then owner of Highfield Nurseries, was also experimenting with plum cordons and mentioned them in his 1985 catalogue. It was gratifying to know that a leading horticulturist was undertaking similar research.

I planted my first plum cordons in 1985. The first three were 'Marjorie's Seedling', 'Kirke's Blue' (subsequently discovered to be 'Old Greengage') and 'Giant Prune'. I chose these three cultivars because they are relatively short jointed and this seemed to be a sensible way to start. During the first growing season of 1986 I did not allow the trees to flower and they quickly established themselves and grew well. I noticed that the growth was more vigorous than that of my cordon apples and pears and this meant that I would probably not be able to give them only one summer pruning as with the other fruit, but would need to deal with them on a more regular basis so as to control the more vigorous growth. I found that pinching back all growth to one bud every three to four weeks during the growing season kept the trees to a relatively well-trained shape. To prevent disease such as silver leaf, I made sure that I did not undertake any pinching out after the end of September and so far this precaution has been successful. Out of the 10 cordon plums that I now grow none has suffered any disease.

In the spring of 1987 these three trees flowered for the first time and to my utter amazement each tree was completely covered with flowers; in fact, it was practically impossible to see anything of the trees but the flowers. What a bonus! As plums generally flower early, I covered the trees every night to ensure that no frost would damage the blossom, and this paid off because before long each tree was covered with a large amount of fruitlets. Not wishing to overload the trees in their first year of fruiting but wishing to experiment at the same time, I thinned two of them and left the 'Giant Prune' unthinned.

As the summer of 1987 was hot, I regularly irrigated the trees to ensure that lack of water would not stress them and thus cause a rejection of much of the fruit they were carrying, something to which I find plums to be particularly susceptible. All three trees continued to carry and produce a good crop with very good fruit size, even the 'Giant Prune' which had been left unthinned. So far the experiment was proving to be very successful and therefore I resolved to plant more plum cordons.

The winter of 1987 saw me planting 'Edwards', 'Imperial Gage' (syn. 'Denniston's Superb), 'Oullins Gage', 'Shropshire Damson' (syn. 'Prune') and 'Victoria', giving me a total of eight plum cordons. My experience with this further planting was similar to the original batch – trees which produced a fine crop of good-sized fruits early in their life. This was followed by 'Cambridge Gage' and 'Czar' a couple of years ago. All my plum cordons are growing well and when the frost allows they produce good crops, with the original trees showing no signs of reduced vigour.

To emphasise the ease of growing plum cordons, I must explain that they receive no special treatment. As a relatively organic grower I do not spray any

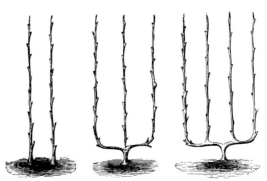

Figs. 12, 13 and 14. VARIOUS CORDON PLUMS.

In the 18th and 19th centuries growers experimented with plum cordons. One such experiment is shown here taken from Fruit Culture for Amateurs *(2nd edition 1898)*

of my fruit and, in the case of the plums, the only pest deterrents I use are plum fruit moth traps which trap the male moths in the same way as codling moth traps are used by apple growers to trap male codling moths. The plum cordons (as well as the rest of my fruit) receive a large handful of blood, fish and bone every February and every three years I give a dressing of stable manure. I try to protect against frost damage by overhead irrigation and ensure that in time of drought all trees receive water.

Growing plums in this way is so easy that it is hard to understand why this form of cordon growing has not been widely publicised by the horticultural press. There do not seem to be many disadvantages using this method, and the advantages surely outweigh them. Having grown plum cordons for nearly 10 years I feel qualified to recommend this method and, following lectures I have given, there are now a number of gardeners following my example.

To me the advantages are consider-able and simple – a large number of plums can be grown in a small garden (my trees are planted 1m [3ft] apart in London clay), the trees come into production at an early stage, they are very attractive to look at when in flower and they produce regular crops of good-sized fruit. The disadvantages are few – due to their weaker growth they are not particularly attactive to look at when dormant (hardly of major importance) and they need regular pinching out rather than an annual prune, which to many people is a distinct advantage!

I thoroughly recommend that you experiment with growing plums in this way. You have nothing to lose – in fact you might well find this method of raising plums quite successful! I am now experimenting with growing cordon cherries and peaches – but that will be the subject of another article some time!

GERALD EDWARDS, amateur fruit grower, exhibitor and judge, is a member of the RHS Fruit Group Committee

Changing Designs for Orchards

PETER DODD

SINCE THE SECOND volume of *Fruit Present and Future* was published by the Royal Horticultural Society just over 20 years ago there have been considerable changes in the planting systems adopted by commericial growers in this country.

These changes have occurred as a result of increased competition from abroad and a move to a greater proportion of fruit being marketed through supermarkets. Both of these influences have meant that growers in this country have had to reduce production costs as far as possible and adopt planting systems that allow the production of both high yields and good fruit quality.

APPLES

In the early 1970s our two main commercial cultivars of apple were 'Cox's Orange Pippin' and 'Bramley's Seedling', both of which were mostly produced on relatively large trees planted in single rows with grass alleys between the rows. In the case of 'Cox', the clone most used was the EMLA clone (a clone selected in the East Malling Long Ashton scheme) but some growers were trying selections with more colour in an attempt to improve the proportion of fruit in the top grade. Nowadays, almost all commercial growers use a coloured clone known as 'Queen Cox'. 'Bramley's Seedling' on the other hand is still used more or less in its original form.

Twenty or so years ago, growers were mostly using fairly vigorous rootstocks for apples. Bush trees on M2 were still being used for both 'Cox's Orange Pippin' and 'Bramley's Seedling' although in the early 70s, many changed to the less vigorous MM106 for new plantings, especially of 'Cox'. During the 1970s and into the early 80s, MM106 became almost the standard rootstock with centre leader 'Cox' trees commonly planted in single rows at spacings of 5.5 x 3.7m (18 x 12ft), a density of 398 trees per hectare (161 trees per acre),

or 4.5 x 3m (15 x 10ft) with 717 trees per hectare (290 trees per acre). Some growers chose the more dwarfing M26 as a rootstock for 'Cox' but experience showed that this combination only worked well on relatively light soils. On stronger soils there were problems of excessive bare wood and a poor balance between vegetative growth and fruit bud formation and this restricted its more general use. M26 has, however, proved to be a good rootstock for 'Bramley' with orchards being planted at around 4.5 x 3m (15 x 10ft) – 717 trees per hectare (290 trees per acre).

As the need increased in the early 80s to produce higher yields and a greater proportion of class 1 fruit, higher density planting of much smaller centre leader trees started to be used by more and more growers. Scientific research both in this country and elsewhere, together with experience of a range of intensive plantings in Europe, had shown that such systems, if well managed, could result in considerably better yields of class 1 fruit; such fruits needing to be of good size (both dessert and culinary) and well coloured in a coloured dessert cultivar such as 'Cox'. With the larger, more widely spaced trees, only fruits borne in the outer part of the canopy where light levels were good, developed as top grade fruit while those from the shaded parts of the tree were both too small and lacked colour. The use of smaller trees eliminated the heavily shaded areas within the tree. As long as these dwarf trees were planted in such a way as to avoid mutual shading and a balance between vegetative growth and fruit bud formation was maintained, a higher proportion of class 1 fruit resulted. The rootstock most

Examples of some of the orchard systems currently used in the UK

Two row bed system

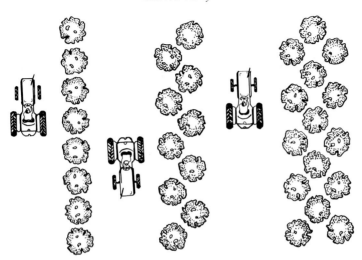

Single row system

Three row bed system

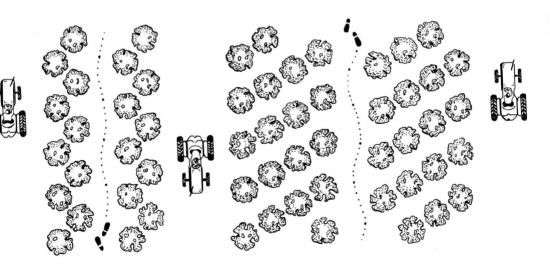

*Four row bed system with
central pathway*

*Eight row bed system
with central pathway*

commonly used for high density plantings is M9, with M27 sometimes being used for more vigorous cultivars such as 'Bramley'.

Over the last 15 years or so, growers using intensive systems for apples have tended to move away from single row to multirow bed systems, the first of which to become popular was the three row bed system with trees trained as North Holland spindles. Within this system, trees were planted at a density of around 3,000 to 3,500 trees per hectare (1214-1417 trees per acre).

As growers and advisers have become more experienced with intensive systems a range of high density plantings have developed and are currently being used in the industry.

The area of commercial apple production has declined over the last 20 years with the area of dessert cultivars dropping from 21,547 ha (53,242 acres) in 1973 to 11,991 ha (26,629 acres) in 1993. The trend in gross production over the period has dropped from approximately 250,000 tonnes in 1973 to around 175,000 tonnes in the mid eighties and back up to 200,000 tonnes by 1993. On a gross production per hectare basis, yield was around 11.5t/ha (4.6 t/acre), dropping to 11t/ha (4.4 t/acre) in the late 70s and climbing to approximately 16 t/ha (6.4 t/acre) by 1993. Much of this improved yield is due to higher density systems. Over the same period, gradeout (of 'Cox' in particular) has improved steadily from around 50 to 60 per cent class 1 in the 70s to 70 to 80 per cent in the 90s.

The area of culinary apples has dropped from 12,729 to 7,300 ha (31,453 – 18,038 acres) over the period 1973 to 1993 while overall gross produc-

tion has increased from about 160,000 tonnes in 1973, dropping to 140,000 tonnes in the early 80s but then rising to 175,000 tonnes in the early 90s. This increase in gross production from a diminishing area is reflected in gross yield figures of around 12.5 t/ha (5.1 t/acre) in 1973, almost doubling to 23t/ha (9.3 t/acre) at present. Much of this increase in yield per hectare is due to the move from large, widely spaced trees at the beginning of the period to the higher density plantings of more dwarfed trees currently used.

Over the 20-year period imports of apples have increased from 42 per cent in 1973 to 55 per cent in 1993.

PEARS

Over the last 20 years or so our main commercial cultivars have been 'Conference', 'Doyenné du Comice' and 'Williams' Bon Chrétien'. Formerly these were mostly grown on Quince A rootstock but more recent plantings have been of trees on the more dwarfing and precocious rootstock Quince C. Bush trees of 'Conference' on Quince A were commonly planted at spacing of around 4.5 x 3.7m (15 x 12ft) while the more upright cultivars were planted closer together at around 4.5 x 2.4m (15 x 8ft). However, centre leader training systems allowed closer spacings and planting distances of between 3 and 3.7m (10 x 12ft) between rows and sometimes as close as 1.2 to 1.5m (4-5ft) in the row, although with spindlebushes 2.1 to 2.6m (7-8½ft) x 4 to 4.3m (13-14ft) became more common. Unlike apples, no very dwarfing rootstock is as yet available for pears, so high density plantings have not generally developed as quickly. In the absence of dwarfing rootstocks, plant growth regulators have been used to help control the trees and have encouraged some growers to try multi-row bed systems of superspindles, or vertical cordons, similar to those used for apples, or a V system consisting of single rows of trees planted between 1 and 1.25m (3-4ft) apart along the row with 3.5m (11½ft) between the rows – 925 to 1,156 trees per hectare (375-468 trees per acre).

As with apples, the area of commercial pear production in the UK has decreased over the last 20 years from 5,218 ha (12,894 acres) in 1973 to an estimated 3,503 ha (8,656 acres) in 1993. Over the period, there was an initial increase in gross production followed by a decline with approximately 40,000 tonnes being produced in the early 70s, rising to nearer 50,000 in the early 80s and then dropping to about 35,000 tonnes at present. In terms of gross production per hectare there has been only a small increase over the period with about 7.5t/ha (3t/acre) being produced in the early 70s, increasing to 12t/ha (4.9 t/acre) in the 80s and dropping to 10t/ha (4t/acre) in the 90s. Although many aspects of pear husbandry have improved over the years an analysis of the trend suggests yields per hectare are not being increased at a sufficient rate by enough growers to maintain gross production. Since 1973 imports of pears have risen dramatically from about 52 per cent to 76 per cent at present.

PLUMS

The main cultivar produced by commercial plum growers is 'Victoria' which in the early 70s represented about a third of the total production in the UK subsequently rising to nearer one half at present. 'Marjorie's Seedling' is the next most commonly grown cultivar. In the early 70s, many established plum orchards consisted of widely spaced trees either on 'Myrobalan B' or 'Pershore' rootstocks. However, as new plum orchards were planted, growers tended to opt for the more dwarfing rootstock 'St Julien A' and this is now used quite widely.

Many of these orchards are planted as single row systems at spacings of approximately 5 x 3.5m (15 x 11½ft) which represents 571 trees per hectare (231 trees per acre). An alternative to the single row system is to use double row beds which increases the density to around 700 trees per hectare (283 trees per acre) at similar spacings, thereby increasing production per hectare. The more dwarfing plum rootstock 'Pixy' is being used in some more recent plantings with several growers experimenting with it in bed systems although its more general acceptance may be limited by its effect on fruit size.

Over the last 20 years or so, the area of commercial plum production in the UK has decreased to almost a third of that in the early 70s. In 1973 the area was 6,037 ha (14,917 acres) while in 1993 it was estimated to be 2,166 ha (5,358 acres). Gross annual production has fallen steadily over the period from over 40,000 to 17,000 tonnes in 1993. The change to more dwarfing rootstocks and higher density planting systems are two factors that have allowed growers to increase yields from about 6 to 8.5t/ha (2.4-3.4 t/acre) but the demand for plums has declined over the last 15 years which clearly restricts prospects for expansion.

CHERRIES

Unlike apples, pears and plums, cherry production has never been dominated by just a few cultivars, most orchards featuring a range to extend marketing opportunities. Similarly, over the last 20 years, no new apple, pear or plum cultivar has dominated those industries whereas with cherries several new cultivars from breeders in this country and overseas are now grown commercially. Sadly, though, the situation with rootstocks is not as dynamic. In the early 70s the only available rootstock suitable for our conditions was *Prunus avium*. Although some trees were on seedling forms of this rootstock, most growers were using clonal material and the East Malling selection F12/1 in particular. Whichever form of *P. avium* was being used, trees were planted at very wide spacings in order to accommodate their vigorous growth. Cherry orchards established before the 70s tended to be planted 'on the square' with distances between the trees of 10.7 to 15.25m (35 - 50ft) representing 133 to 93 trees per hectare (54 - 38 trees per acre). Such orchards took a long time before they started to crop and therefore growers often interplanted them in a quincunx design. Usually these filler trees were removed as the main ones became established but sometimes they were not, creating very dense orchards. By the 70s though, the few growers that were planting cherries were adopting more permanent rectangular designs with trees at 6.5 x 5m (21.3 x 15ft) or 307 trees per hectare (124 trees per acre).

During the late 70s, a new semi-dwarfing rootstock from East Malling Research Station became available to growers. This rootstock, named 'Colt' was selected for new plantings and now is the most common used in the industry. Although not having a great dwarfing effect, it has allowed trees to be planted at closer spacings and higher densities, 5 x 3.5m (15 x 11½ft) which is 571 trees per hectare (231 trees per acre) being typical for a single row system and densities around 700 trees per hectare (283 trees per acre) for double row systems. The area of cherries grown commercially in the UK has decreased dramatically over the last 20 or so years from 2,664 ha (6,583 acres) in 1973 to an estimated 772 ha (1,908 acres) in 1993. Many of the reasons for this decline are related to large trees and their difficult management. The more dwarfing rootstock allows, for instance, easier spraying, harvesting and pruning as well as the possibility of netting the fruiting trees against birds. As can be expected from such a decline in crop area since 1973, gross production has fallen almost as dramatically from about 8,000 tonnes being produced in 1973 to around 3,000 tonnes in the early 90s. Yields per hectare have only increased slightly from 3t/ha (1.2t/acre) in the early 70s to 3.5t/ha (1.4t/acre) now. Demand for cherries has remained fairly constant and the shortfall in home production has been replaced by imports which have increased from around 2,000 tonnes to 9,000 tonnes at present. In 1973, 90 per cent of the crop was home produced, while now it is a mere 23 per cent.

Looking to the future, the requirement to produce a high proportion of top quality fruit will almost certainly continue and therefore the eradication of orchards on more marginal sites will inevitably follow. With the industry focusing on the most favoured sites, production has to be optimised, which most likely will involve a more general use of high density planting systems. The choice of system not only depends on technology but also on economics and systems that do emerge in the future are likely to be those that are the most robust in fluctuating economic climates. There are also, of course, environmental pressures and again systems adopted must be able to withstand changes in legislation, some of which may be introduced at very short notice.

The future, therefore is challenging, but with careful consideration and planning there is no reason why the industry cannot expand to reduce the impact of imports during our main season.

PETER DODD lectures in Fruit Production at the University of London's Wye College and is a member of the RHS Fruit Group Committee

Do Windbreaks Improve Fruit?

SHEILA BAXTER

ON THE FACE OF IT, fruit does not seem to need windbreaks, as most of our fruit plants appear very hardy. However, a lot of the damage caused by wind is so insidious that it goes unseen.

The 'Cox's Orange Pippin' apple is the most widely grown cultivar in the United Kingdom, but it is extremely sensitive to variation in climate. If regular yields of good quality fruit are required, the climate has to be modified as much as possible. To show how much the climate matters, two adjacent 'Cox' orchards in Kent were monitored – one with windbreaks, the other without. The difference was a 10 per cent greater yield and a crop of far better quality in the sheltered orchard. In another year and a different orchard, increases of up to 82 per cent were recorded.

Pears are notorious for simply not cropping if they are rocked by wind, as their roots are very brittle and easily broken, so it is easy to understand the 100 per cent increase in yield recorded where windbreaks have been used. One 'Conference' orchard in Kent had not cropped in all its 10-year life before the grower's patience snapped and he declared that he was wasting his money and was going to salvage the stakes and grub out the orchard. But when the trees were examined they were found to be supporting the stakes instead of the other way round, and they were so unstable that it would have taken little effort to have pushed them over! After they had been re-staked firmly and some windbreaks had been provided, the orchard was soon cropping as heavily as the one next to it, which had had windbreaks all the time.

Trees on weaker rootstocks need permanent staking, but even they are not safe if they are exposed to strong winds and are blown about on wet soils, as a swivel hole forms and when it rains the hole fills with water. If the hole is left, the tree either drowns because the smooth sides of the hole cannot allow the water to drain away or the tree falls over from being blown about, as happened in the hurricane of 1987.

The financial loss is not only in the cost of the trees, but the loss of the crop for several years to come while replacements are established and come into bearing. Quality of fruit is also affected by wind damage, especially with pears. This is reflected in both the quantity of fruit in the top grade and the price it receives.

The most commonly seen symptom of damage by cold winds is russeting on fruit which would otherwise have a smooth skin, especially around the stalk end of apples. This often leads to cracking, since the skin cannot expand as the fruit grows, and it is then either downgraded or rejected, depending on the severity of the condition. Severe and prolonged cold wind around blossom time can desiccate flower stalks and whole clusters may fall, resulting in no crop in the worst years. If the blossom stays on the trees, cold winds can also prevent pollination, either by damaging the reproductive parts of the flowers, or by desiccating the pollen. Even if there is no visible damage, low temperatures from the chilling effect of wind can prevent growth of the pollen down the style to the ovaries. This can lead to little or no crop, or if partial pollination has occurred, the fruit may be misshapen.

Early-flowering fruits such as plums and pears are particularly prone to damage from cold winds, though 'Conference' pear can set fruit without pollination, being parthenocarpic, but the fruit tends to be sausage-shaped. Another reason for poor crops can be the absence of pollinating insects. Most insects, particularly honey bees, like warm air with low wind speeds if they are to work well, so a sheltered crop is infinitely preferable to one receiving the full force of the wind.

Developing fruit needs adequate temperatures for cell division in the early stages. Cold wind at this crucial time can result in small fruits. Also, fruit is easily damaged if it rubs on another fruit or a branch and, later in the season, it can be blown off before harvest. This is particularly the case with pears, which seem to mature overnight!

Leaf tattering can deplete plant reserves and the ability to photosynthesise properly. People often seem surprised that soft fruit should need windbreaks, but leaf tattering considerably reduces the following year's crop. Fruit reduction in blackcurrants can be in the order of 25 per cent and raspberries can lose 20 per cent or more of their crop. Raspberry cultivars with long laterals can lose much more than 20 per cent of the fruit if strong winds break the laterals before fruiting.

Strawberries, being close to the ground, are not thought to suffer from wind damage, but near the sea the leaves are frequently burnt off by salt-laden winds and this depletes reserves and affects cropping in that year and probably the following one also, unless the plants have a very good growing season in which to make good the loss. Wind damage to the young strawberry leaves in September/October, when flowers for the next year's crop are being initiated, is known to reduce cropping – sometimes quite drastically.

At the Scottish Crop Research Institute, unsheltered and sheltered strawberry plants were measured and the following increases in yield were found in the sheltered plants:

Leaves + 20%
Crowns + 24%
Trusses + 26%
Runners + 25%

Yield increases from sheltered plants ranged from 7 per cent to a staggering 77 per cent over a seven-year period of monitoring.

Where windbreaks are provided, the soil temperature can be as much as 3°C (5°F) higher than unprotected soil, so crops often mature earlier.

Windbreaks can also benefit crops grown in greenhouses and plastic clad tunnels. Not only is there a reduction in structural damage, but considerable fuel savings can be made – up to 30 per cent – which can be very important where early fruit crops, such as strawberries, are being grown. And these are not the only benefits. With protection temperatures are more uniform across greenhouses so plant growth is less variable and yields are increased.

Obviously the more tender fruits such as peaches, nectarines, grapes and figs need warm, sunny and sheltered growing conditions when they are grown outside, but perhaps more consideration should be given to sheltering our common fruits, which are so often taken for granted. However, a solid wall is not the ideal, as it causes turbulence on the leeward side. The best windbreaks are 50 per cent permeable, so that the wind can pass through them at a greatly reduced speed.

SHEILA BAXTER, a former member of the Ministry's Advisory Service (ADAS), is a member of the RHS Fruit Group Committee

Honeybees and Pollination

KARL SHOWLER

TODAY, WE WOULD all accept the simple statement that opens the Ministry of Agriculture, Fisheries and Food leaflet 328, (1971): 'adequate pollination is an essential preliminary to the production of a good crop for most kinds of fruit trees'. Yet this was not always so, pollen was believed by educated beekeepers and horticulturists to be the source of beeswax or crystalline honey and it was not associated with the creation of seed. Even when the function of pollen became clear the need for adequate cross pollination between cultivars was not appreciated. I would like to explore the confused path down which beekeepers and fruit growers stumbled, at very considerable financial cost, to establish the first extensive commercial orchards in the USA.

> Brush'd from each anther's crown,
> the mealy gold,
> With morning dew, the light
> fang'd artists mould,
> Fill with the foodful load their hollow'd thigh,
> And to their nurslings bear the rich supply
> The Bees (lines 251- 4)

So wrote Dr John Evans, senior physician at the Salop Infirmary, Shrewsbury, in his epic poem *The Bees* (1806). In his notes Evans explained the background to his verses and in this case drew attention to the confusion between the pollen found in flowers and that seen on bees. The latter was often called 'farina' and was believed to be the source of beeswax or crystalline honey and the 'beebread' upon which bees fed their larvae.

In the ancient world there was speculation as to where wax came from. In BC 344 the Greek philosopher and scientist Aristotle suggested that bees collected wax from flowers. Clearly beekeepers were confusing pollen collection with the production of beeswax in the hive by the bees themselves. Two thousand years later this confusion persisted. The English writer Edmund Southerne explained why it was bad practice to move strong colonies from comb-filled skeps (hives made of straw) to new empty ones, for as he put it: 'They are forced to gather waxe and a'new work it'.

Southerne's extremely observant contemporary, the Reverend Charles Butler (*Feminine Monarchy*, 1609), distinguished wax from pollen even if he did not know of their different origins. He also recorded seeing wax scales around his skeps and observed bees masticating scales and constructing comb. Butler gathered these scales and noted that they were soft and pliable, unlike pollen which was 'mutterable' i.e. crumbled and did not fuse together when warmed. Butler thought that pollen on the bees legs was one source of honey but he also knew that nectar was collected by bees for he found it in their honey sacs. He also recognised that honey was stored by the bees in both liquid and crystalline forms. To us these conclusions seem confusing, but we must remember that until the middle of the 19th century there was no satisfactory way of constructing beehives that permitted the waxen combs to be replaced after examination so Butler had little opportunity of observing in detail what went on between the combs.

A generation later there was still confusion. In 1637 Richard Remnant wrote of what we now recognise as pollen gathering:

'They gather wax all the yeere,
from the first gathering to the last,
from the willow to the blowing ivie. . .
The wax gathered of the flowers or
bloomes with the fangs of the Bee,
and so she puts it onto her thighs, and
rubs one against the other to fasten it
on and then carries it home, and
makes the combs in their hives.'

The great French naturalist De Réaumur (1740) continued the link between pollen and wax in suggesting the wax was generated by a digestive or fermentive process within the bee. However, in 1744 the German, H C Hornbostel, suggested the wax scales, originated under flaps on the underside of the abdomen into which it would be impossible to insert scales if they were gathered from flowers. Hornbostel, following the conventions of his generation, published under the pseudonym Melittophilus Theosebastus in an obscure German journal *Hamburg Vermis*

Bibiliothek (2:46-62) which had a limited circulation so his work did not get wide recognition. As Hornbostel made his observations in Germany, so B Cooke in Britain described the effect the farina of different sorts of apple trees had on the fruit of a neighbouring tree (*Phil. Trans.* 43: 169, 1745).

By the end of the 18th century John Hunter, the eminent entomologist, concluded that as pollen was multi-coloured it could not be the source of new white wax. Hunter's trials also showed that bees could draw wax even if they were not bringing in pollen. By showing that pollen was not the source of wax he led to the thought that dominated 19th century research that sugar was its source and therefore pollen had some other function.

If during the 18th century workers had attempted to determine the floral source of wax, those working in the 19th century either followed Hunter and the Swiss Huber down the new 'Sugar' path or attempted to disprove the latter's careful experiments.

Dr Edward Bevan MD, brought together in *The Honey-bee*, 1827, a vast amount of information from Britain and Europe on the honeybee including its use of pollen. He maintained a nationwide correspondence with eminent apiarians and horticulturists including Thomas A Knight, President of the Royal Horticultural Society, and backed up his extensive reading with his own observations. However, although he recognised the importance of pollen as the basis of the food for bee larvae there was not, in his generation, a pollination problem in the flower-rich countryside or in orchards with many cultivars.

In the USA and Canada the mid-century books on beekeeping, while drawing on the British and European experience, focused on their own rapid technological developments including the moveable comb hive that permitted a range of manipulations and observations not possible with fixed comb hives. At that time most authors came from the northern states to the east of the Mississippi where, until the turn of the century, there seemed to be limitless bee pasturage.

Frank Cheshire's massive two volume (1886 & 1888) summation of British beekeeping, *Bees and Beekeeping*, devoted 49 pages of volume 1 to a wide ranging review of 'Bees as fertilisers, florists and fruit producers'. Cheshire's work reflected the current preoccupation with the botanical aspects of pollination, and honey yields rather than pollination. He also drew attention to the honeybees' agricultural importance but left this as a simple undeveloped statement:

> 'A new consideration now awaits us: Bees are not only florists – they are fruit-producers; our orchard and fruit crops and leguminous seed, constituting together no inconsiderable fraction of human food, are very largely dependant upon insect agency, and the fee paid for professional attendance on the part of the little inoculator is nectar.'

In 1875 the Old Dominion Fruit Company had planted 22,000 standard 'Bartlett' pear trees at Scotland on the James River, Virginia. For 15 years according to J H Lovell (*The Flower and the Bee*, 1919) the trees bloomed well but set insignificant crops. However, when American pomologist M B Waite visited the plantation in 1892 he noticed that where any 'Bartlett' trees had died out and been replaced with either 'Clapp's Favourite' or 'Buffum' the surrounding trees were as heavily laden with fruit as adjoining mixed orchards. Lovell cites many other examples of defective pollination due to failure to provide for crossing between compatible cultivars and from the beekeeper's point of view showed how honeybees were needed to effect pollen movement.

If the British were still living in a world of apicultural innocence by 1890, in the USA the danger to bees from agricultural sprays had reared its toxic head. The A I Root Company's *ABC of Bee Culture* for 1905 contained an extended summary of the dangers facing bees. It drew on the 1894 volume of their magazine *Gleanings in Bee Culture* where a series of articles highlighted the problem of bee losses so significant that certain States had adopted regulations against spraying insecticides on open crop blossoms. The problems facing fruit growers and beekeepers attracted interest at several American research stations where experiments demonstrated both the need for honeybees and the damage insecticides did to their adult and larval stages. By 1917 B N Gates wrote in the *Massachusetts Horticultural Society Transactions* (1:71-88):

> 'He may fertilize, and cultivate the soil, prune, thin and spray the trees, in a word he may do all of those things which modern practice advocates, yet without his pollinating agents, chief among which are the honey bees, to transfer pollen from the stamens to the pistil of the blooms, his crop may fail.'

By the early 1920s in the USA and Canada, a beekeeping industry was

continues after colour

Apricot 'Moor Park' is a fine old cultivar still available today (see p33 'Flavoursome Fruits'). This painting by William J Hooker first appeared in Hooker's Finest Fruits, *1815, proving the cultivar has been in cultivation for over 180 years*

(OPPOSITE PAGE) the summer fruit tortrix caterpillar causes widespread damage (see bottom left) to apples. This caterpillar (top left) has been exposed to the juvenile insect growth regulator, fenoxycarb, which causes growth deformities and eventual death. If untreated the caterpillar will grow to the summer fruit tortrix moth (centre) which is one of the most troublesome pests of apples (see p93, 'Pest and Disease Management in Commercial Fruit Production')

TOP: Gooseberry 'Invicta' is a more recent culti-var bred for resistance to American gooseberry mildew (see 'The Golden Years of Fruit p33)

ABOVE: 'Williams' Bon Chrétien, is a well known old pear that is still readily available and remains widely planted (see p33)

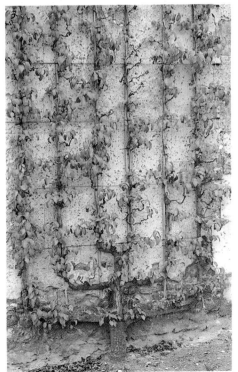

TOP: *part of the frame area in the Potager. Unlike frames in the British sense, these are more mini-greenhouses as they are a metre (3ft) or so tall at the back to accommodate aubergines and peppers. They would normally only be closed early and late in the season for extra warmth*

ABOVE: *although this 'Doyenné du Comice' pear espalier looks as though it may have been in the original planting, it is only 30 to 40 years old*

LEFT: *a six branch palmette verrier pear tree grown against a wall. This favoured position is normally saved for the choicer dessert cultivars which benefit most from the extra warmth and sunlight.*

See p14 for account of RHS Fruit Group's visit to the Potager du Roi, Versailles.

TOP: *the Model Fruit Gardens at Wisley today (see p74) – on the left are columnar apple trees while netting encloses the gooseberry collection*

ABOVE: Malus zumi *(centre) has proved an important donor of mildew resistance for apples such as these second backcross commercial derivatives (see p110 for HRI's developing programme of pest and disease resistant apples)*

RIGHT: *Growing plums as cordons has proved very successful for one amateur grower (see p51). These cordons covered in blossom are heavy with fruit each year*

BELOW: 'Glenora' (left) is a moderately early grape with a Labrusca flavour. 'Perlette' (centre) is an early which ripens in Belgium in late August. 'Venus' (right) has a hint of strawberry or raspberry in taste (see p25 for 'Success with Seedless')

ABOVE: This collection of the grapes trialled by Peter Bauwens in Belgium highlights the variety of sizes and colours of the berries (see p25)

LEFT: this yellow-fruited primocane raspberry selection has performed well at East Malling. Although the texture and colour in yellow types tend to deteriorate rapidly after picking, selection is continuing for improving the quality of texture and flavour (see p84)

BOTTOM: 'Autumn Bliss' (right) was HRI, East Malling's first primocane raspberry release in 1983 and remains one of the most popular in Britain. 'Autumn Britten' (left), trialled at 3676/6, has performed well in Canada (see p84)

established with operations based on 100 hive units, with a few colonies per beekeeper on farms or in backlots of rural towns still remaining for domestic use. However in Britain and Ireland there was as yet no large scale industry. The British beekeeper was more likely to be a town dweller with work that allowed time off in the day, although for the last 50 years beekeeping had been linked to the concept of '5 acres and a cow' and rural self sufficiency.

Modern beekeeping with moveable comb hives, rather than fixed comb skeps, falls into two phases; the early phase when it was not easy to move numbers of bee hives and the later phase after the advent of motorised transport.

It is true that beekeepers had always moved colonies, either in skeps or later in wooden hives, but only in small numbers. In Europe and Britain there was a long tradition of taking bees to the moors to get heather honey. The bees were taken by horsedrawn carts from the lowlands to the moors, the outward journey lasting one or two days; the beekeeper remaining on site overnight returning next day. In the larger American operations each apiary was manned throughout the season by a hired hand who lived in a shanty or with a local family. Once established the apiary was run as a self-contained unit only the honey being removed at the season's end. Transport difficulties meant that large numbers of colonies were kept in one place although this led to rapidly declining returns from over population coupled with the removal of high yielding natural nectar sources, such as *Tilia americana* (American lime) and forage crops such as buckwheat *(Fagopyrum*

esculentum), to make way for grain crops.

In Europe and the USA the rivers were also used to move colonies and on the Mississippi in 1878 C O Perrine, a major honey exporter, adapted a river steamboat towing two barges as a floating apiary. His idea was to follow the blooming season up the river from south to north although as the expedition moved up river it became clear this was more complex than anticipated. The expedition was dogged by mechanical failures, yellow fever and loss of bees from their being blown into the water by adverse winds when the hives were open. In fact the journey took two years to complete, costing Perine a great deal of money.

Movement by rail became common once the railways started to expand. There was a considerable fuss in Britain over this movement in the 1870s but I have found no record of the first consignments. From the rail or water wharf the hives were moved by horsedrawn carts. Several Americans developed freight car movements from one crop to another but in the end found labour costs too high.

In his book *Outapiaries* (1919) Maurice G Dadant said prophetically:
> 'The Automobile has done more than any other one thing to revolutionise outapiary beekeeping. Its adaptability to extensive beekeeping is self evident. It furnishes a quick mode of travel from one apiary to another, it travels in heat as well as in cooler weather, it removes the danger of stings to horses when used in the apiary.'

It is difficult to imagine what Dadant would make of one of the modern American articulated 18-wheel

trucks moving 600 pallet-mounted colonies at a time between pollination contracts.

Since Dadant's time the knowledge supporting beekeeping and pollination has become increasingly sophisticated. Between the two World Wars the basic patterns were established. The horse soon disappeared as did the resident apiary attendant, for the car and truck made rapid movement and inspection of colonies possible. By 1928 *Gleanings in Bee Culture* was advising beekeepers to remove their colonies from orchards after flowering to reduce spray damage.

Even in Britain where far fewer crops need pollinating than in the USA, by the late 1930s beekeepers were moving several thousand colonies to fruit orchards and to other seed crops to augment existing bee populations. Over the next 15 years there was a steady reduction in permanent farm-owned colonies as these suffered most from insecticides. To all beekeepers in arable areas the question of bee loss by insecticidal sprays was a constant and increasing worry so beekeepers' associations made regular representations to Government. If at one time beekeepers seemed to be alone in recognising the spray problem they are now but a small section of a great lobby that seeks to maintain a balance between insect pest control and beneficial insect survival.

In the 50 years since the RHS Fruit Group came into being growers' understanding of their crops' requirements has deepened; the amount of information in the works of J B Free (UK) *Insect Pollination of Crops* (1970) and S E McGregor (USA) *Insect Pollination of Cultivated Crop Plants* (1976) is so daunting that I suspect each grower is forced to be selective in their reading.

In the USA a range of bees other than the honeybee have been brought into 'cultivation' as their special role as pollinators to certain crops was recognised even in the interwar period. Today in Britain imported Dutch bumblebees are being used in greenhouses but so far the use of 'otherbees' is more of a curiosity than a practical proposition. However, the amount of new woodlands currently being planted may well encourage the natural buildup of 'otherbee' populations.

And what of the beekeepers? Beekeeping is a small but wide ranging activity with many specialisations; specialists in one field having only a passing knowledge of others. Today's serious beekeeper has so much more scientific information available and detailed knowledge about bees than any of the early apiarians.

In pollination work the beekeeper is more than ever dependent on the grower: the orchard with its balance of cultivars will have been planted years before the bees are needed; the annual crop will have grown to flowering before the bees are needed. Therefore, the beekeeper must co-operate with the grower months ahead to ensure the right sized colonies are in place in time for early crops. This requires suitable advance feeding, hives easy to transport to locations screened from wind and with fresh uncontaminated drinking water available.

In writing this article it has become clear to me that although fruit crops have attracted the attention of beekeepers for over 125 years no-one has pro-duced a book for beekeepers that sets out clearly and in balance both the api-cultural techniques and the crop cul-tural requirements involved. Moving bees to pollination is, if mentioned at all, treated as a subsection of a general text. The type of publication needed is similar to that of Stanley B Whitehead's *Bees to the Heather* (1954) in which he brought together useful information on most aspects of this crop. In 1986 a simi-lar wide ranging approach was adopted by Allan Calder in *Oilseed Rape and Bees* for what is now Britain's major honey crop but one which needs special han-dling and honey treatment.

KARL SHOWLER, President of the British Beekeeper's Association for 1989-90, was for-merly on the staff of the International Bee Research Association and is now an anti-quarian book dealer.

Brogdale Horticultural Trust

JOAN MORGAN

THE NATIONAL FRUIT Collections at Brogdale, near Faversham in Kent, are one of our great treasures, yet until recently they were comparatively unknown to the general public. The Royal Horticultural Society's Fruit Col-lections at Wisley are widely known and admired for their superb range of culti-vars, but the considerably larger and more diverse National Collections, which were part of the Ministry of Agri-culture's Experimental Horticulture Sta-tion and the National Fruit Trials, were only occasionally open to visitors.

Over the last four years this has changed dramatically. The home for the Collections is now provided by the Brogdale Horticultural Trust, a charitable trust which bought the whole Station from the Ministry in 1991. Since then the general public have been able to walk through orchards of over 2,000 apple cultivars, some 500 pears, 350 plums and 220 cherries, as well as nuts, medlars, quinces and plantations of over 100 gooseberries, together with currants and vines. Visitors can taste and buy rarities, such as 'Lamb Abbey Pearmain', 'Transparent Gage' and 'Frizzled Filbert', and a trip to Brogdale is on every fruit lover's itinerary. But this has not been achieved without heroic determination by the Trust.

Early in 1989 the Government proposed closing Brogdale as part of its reduction in funding to horticultural research and development and the security of these Collections, which are among the largest in the world, was threatened. At a time when there was increasing public awareness of our diminishing genetic resources, as well as nostalgia for the good things of the past, the closure of Brogdale became virtually a national crisis, first brought to prominence in a speech given by HRH the Prince of Wales to the Worshipful Company of Fruiterers in February 1989. The public, as well as the amateur and professional fruit fraternity, were outraged. Brogdale became the subject of numerous press articles and media coverage; more furore could not have been generated if plans had been announced to close the Victoria and Albert Museum or Kew Gardens.

In fact, the Ministry had no intention of abandoning its Collections, but proposed that they be 'moved' to another site and on December 15, 1989, announced that Brogdale would close in March 1990 and that the Collections would be 'moved' to the University of London's Wye College, near Ashford, some 12 miles to the south. 'Moving' the Collections appeared complete madness to the, by now, immensely concerned public. Even to the most experienced fruit grower, the prospect of propagating over 4,000 cultivars was awesome, let alone checking them all when they fruited.

Many different people and groups had been lobbying for Brogdale's survival and this was a near mortal blow, particularly for the local enthusiasts, who included past Director Jack Ingram, member of staff Hugh Ermen, the current Deputy Director Dr David Pennell and myself. We had put together plans for a Trust to manage and develop Brogdale as a heritage centre and in October 1989 had taken our ideas to the local Swale Borough Council. Swale had been in communication with the Ministry over Brogdale's future since the summer and had stressed its interest in the retention of the Collections within the Borough. When we met its Chief Executive, Bill Croydon, and Amenities Officer, Geoff Wade, they too became enthused with the idea that a new fruit centre could be created at Brogdale. The Council needed little persuasion that this international asset could be the foundation of a unique and singularly fitting development for a Borough so committed to fruit – the orchards of the East Kent fruit belt lie in its midst and Sheerness is the largest importing centre of exotic fruit in Britain. Swale entered the debate in early November, but not soon enough to influence the Ministry's decision.

Nevertheless, the embryo Trust persisted, encouraged above all by public support and urged on by Alan Gear and the example of his thriving Henry Doubleday Research Association at Ryton, which only a few years before had been just a green field. The infant Trust believed that a fruit centre could still be made at Brogdale, and this became more probable after 17 January, 1990, when Sir Roger Moate, MP for Faversham, made Brogdale the subject of an adjournment debate. Sir Roger 'argued strongly that the decision to close Brogdale and move the world's biggest fruit Collection to a site 12 miles away was totally wrong and urged the Government to change this decision. If, however, the Government was determined that the collection was moved then he sought assurances. . . that they would support local initiatives to establish a Trust that would operate a splendid new National Fruit Centre – a fruit museum in the heart of the Garden of England – and contribute to the commercial interests of the British fruit industry' on the site at Brogdale. The Minister's response was sympathetic and discussions with Swale were reopened.

The Brogdale Horticultural Trust was formed on 28 Febrary, 1990 with Alan Gear as Acting Chairman. Goodwill and enthusiasm came from every quarter. Lord Selborne, formerly Chairman of the Agricultural and Food Research Council and himself a fruit grower and nurseryman, agreed to join the Trust. I remember going to London to see him in April 1990 with Bill Croydon and David Pennell, and the delight we all felt when Lord Selborne eagerly accepted. Alan Todd, Fruiterer and Chairman of the East Malling Trust for Horticultural Research, also endorsed the plan to conserve Brogdale. The Worshipful Company of Fruiterers took Brogdale to their hearts and pledged their support, adding further credibility to the cause. Lord Selborne became Chairman of the Trust with some 15 trustees and Bill Croydon as Vice Chairman. There was, however, still the hurdle of acquiring the site – 150 acre farms in a prime fruit growing area in Kent do not come cheap! Again the Prince came to the rescue. By May funding was in place: the Duchy of Cornwall, together with Swale Borough Council, provided the mortgage to buy Brogdale.

For a time it looked as if there might be two Collections, the old one at Brogdale and a new one down the road at Wye, but logic prevailed. The Ministry now began to review its decision to 'move' the Collections and, with negotiations aided by the Prince and the Fruiterers, a working compromise was reached. The Collections would remain at Brogdale, under contract to the Ministry and managed by the Trust under the scientific direction of Wye College. It took, however, nearly a year of protracted negotiations before the purchase and agreements were completed in May 1991.

The Brogdale Horticultural Trust was registered in April 1990 and gained charitable status in July 1990. Its staff consisted largely of David Pennell, hired for two days a week from the Ministry (David had been tranferred to the Ministry Station at Efford), plus some part-time and volunteer help. The Fruiterers' Company employed the late Peter Gow as fundraiser and the Trust, sustained by donations from Television South's Charitable Trust, Marks and Spencer, John Lewis, Friends of Brogdale and others, became a reality. It made public appearances at Chelsea and other RHS Shows, Kent County Show, Marden Fruit Show and the first Apple Day. On that Sunday, 21 October, 1990, about 15,000 people came to Covent Garden. We sold our van load of apples by 10.30 am and soon ran out of leaflets, but the queue of people needing information and their apples named never ceased. Television and press coverage from this and other occasions gave the Trust wide publicity and immense encouragement to consolidate its plans and move forward.

The Trust acquired Brogdale on 3 May, 1991, when it was officially opened to the public by Baroness Trumpington, who as junior Minister of Agriculture had been the architect of its closure. David Pennell had taken the brave step of resigning from the Ministry in order to run Brogdale. The Ministry and its skeleton staff now bowed out, with some of them transferring to the Trust, and Wye and the Trust took over the management of the Collections.

Over the past four years thousands of visitors have been guided through the Collections. Many have been almost overwhelmed by their extent, diversity and riches, and several return again and again to try new fruits on sale in the shop and to buy fruit trees for their gardens. Special events, demonstrations and workshops provide further opportunities for learning more about fruit and exploring the Collections. Not only can you see the choicest fruits, but less familiar cultivars such as the ancient 'Api' apple, British curiosities like the

'Knobby Russet' and 'Bloody Ploughman', and in addition a whole range of new cultivars. The Collections have received the best from the Trials and include, for example, the intensely flavoured Dutch crosses between 'Cox's Orange Pippin' and 'Jonathan', such as 'Lucullus', and new Italian pears. You can never cease to wonder at their international breadth, especially among the apples, where you can move from Oregon's 'Orenco' to 'Boston Russet' and 'Niagara' and across to 'Kilkenny Pearmain', 'London Pippin' and 'Belle-Fille Normande' and down to 'Kandil Sinape' and 'Tasman Pride'.

Years of work went into bringing the Collections to this pitch. The late 'Jock' Potter, who was the first Director of the National Fruit Trials and retired in 1972, was chiefly responsible for their formation and systematic order, assisted by the late John Bultitude and Muriel Smith. They achieved, as far as is possible, the goal of 'all cultivars true to name', which has been fruit growers' aim ever since the first international Fruit Collection was made in the Horticultural Society's garden at Chiswick in the early 1800s. The present Collection was begun as part of the first British Commercial (later National) Fruit Trials, established at the RHS Garden, Wisley, in 1922, and Potter became the Society's Fruit Officer in charge of the Trials in 1936, with pomologist, nurseryman and connoisseur Edward Bunyard as his mentor.

During and after the war, Potter benefited from the missionary zeal of Morton Shand, the wine and food writer, who was also a founder member of the RHS Fruit Group. Shand championed the cause of lost apples in articles and broadcasts and, helped by fellow enthusiasts, he enriched not only the Apple but all the Collections. Initially the Collections were funded by the RHS and the Ministry, but after the war they became the Ministry's sole responsibility, and during the 1950s the Collections were transferred to the larger site at Brogdale. At the same time Potter laid out the RHS Fruit Collection at Wisley with a selection of the most renowned cultivars. Since his retirement, the number of cultivars in the Collections has expanded as new material from fruit breeders and trials has been added.

Wye College and the Brogdale Trust will continue to add to the Collections as well as make them widely available for research and reference. The Trust has started an additional Strawberry Collection, sponsored by Safeway plc, and plans are in hand for Citrus and Raspberry Collections. The former Ministry work of Plant Variety Rights testing of apples is now carried out by Wye College, while the Trust is continuing to evaluate fruit cultivars for the fruit industry, as in Ministry days, but with the backing of the Apple and Pear Research Council and the Horticultural Development Council. In collaboration with the RHS, the Trust is also evaluating fruit cultivars for the amateur grower.

Brogdale's staff now includes a Chief Executive, Gerry Oughton, with Dr David Pennell as Horticultural Director and in the wings are the Trustees: Lord Selborne (Chairman); Bill Croydon (Vice Chairman); Alan Todd (Deputy Chairman); Sir David Landale (late Secretary of the Duchy of Cornwall); Master of the Fruiterers, Sir Rowland Whitehead; Swale Borough Councillor, Jean Newman; Dr Stefan Buczacki, Alan Gear, Don Goodwin, Jack Ingram, David Hope Mason, Sir Roger Moate MP, Dr Joan Morgan and Geoffrey Wade.

The 'Friends of Brogdale' was formed in June 1990 to help support Brogdale financially and practically - from fruit adviser to car park attendant. Friends, who are drawn from all over the globe, are kept in touch by a quarterly newsletter *Fruit News* and through Friends' Days and the Friends' Information Line, which is in operation every Friday afternoon. Its Working Party (we have not yet graduated to a formal consitution) include Hugh Ermen, Jack Ingram, Brian Self and Sue White, all bullied by me and helped by David Burd, Lionel Clarke, Bob Sanders, Howard Stringer and, until he moved back to his native Dorset, Robin Stapleton, who was the last Ministry Director of Brogdale.

The Trust now intends to build on its achievements and plans are in hand to expand and develop the Trust's educational role and its visitor centre, as well as extend its research and development work. A key element in the visitor centre will be a complex of fruit gardens, which will highlight the chief periods, countries and influences in the development of today's cultivars and growing techniques, together with a number of modern gardens designed to inspire the amateur. The history of fruit will be explored further in the Richard Harris Museum, which will be located in a group of converted farm buildings. It takes its name from Henry VIII's fruiterer, who established probably the first commercial orchards in Britain at nearby Teynham. Every facet of the story of fruit will be explored, from folk lore and medicine to the commercial production and sale of fruit, and from the role of fruit on the dining table and in the kitchens to cider and perry production. A lecture theatre is planned and the existing plant centre, shop and restaurant will be expanded. The Trust believes that these developments will complement the National Fruit Collections as well as enhancing everyone's

knowledge and appreciation of fruit.

For information contact Brogdale Horticultural Trust, Faversham, Kent ME13 8XZ. Tel: 01795 535286

DR JOAN MORGAN, writer and horticultural historian, is a Trustee of Brogdale Horticultural Trust, a member of the RHS Fruit and Vegetable Committee and co-author with Alison Richards of The Book of Apples

In Search of 'Warrior'

BY JOHN SALE

REPRINTED, WITH minor amendments, from *The Dorset Year Book*, 1994, by kind permission of the former Editor, Mr F Langford.

On 19 March, 1993, I received a telephone call from a colleague living in Folkestone, asking if I knew anything about an apple named 'Warrior': I replied that I was aware of a very sketchy reference in the National Apple Register of the United Kingdom, but nothing else. My colleague, a retired senior police officer and a very dedicated and knowledgeable fruit grower had, with his wife, lunched with me near Dorchester two days previously. After we had paid a visit to the Abbotsbury Gardens he returned to relatives at Iwerne Minster, where he read a reprinted letter in the Dorset Year Book asking 'What has

happened to 'Warrior' apples?'

Knowing my great interest in researching 'lost', old, unrecorded and unusual apple cultivars, he passed the information to me. It was fitting that a policeman, albeit retired, should initiate the detective work that followed!

The Year Book at the Dorset County Library revealed the editor's name and that of the publishers. The editor was most helpful especially in telephoning the owners of four 'Warrior' trees, in two locations, and then introducing me to them.

After initial examinations of the four trees, when I took scionwood for grafting, I made further visits to examine blossom from the first four trees, and also three others in three additional locations.

When I examined all the blossom, I

was forced to come to the undeniable conclusion that three different apple cultivars had been very reliably reported to me as being 'Warrior'.

One tree, which has remained the odd man out throughout, had a pale pink on white blossom with a long stalk, whereas the other six all had very short stalks and are not only equally divided into two very distinct blossom combinations, but are in widely differing flowering groups. The earliest has brilliant crimson on white blossom, the latest a slight dull crimson flush on a pale cream base.

The position of the male and female parts of the flowers of the six are similar in their variance, and self fertility may exist (but this has yet to be proven).

I was informed of two more trees in different locations by the time I began to gather and compare mature leaves, but the blossom being over, I will not be able to type them until next year; suffice to say however that the leaves of the eight are similar, ovate to long and upfolded.

The identification of apple cultivars is an exact science, in which the leaves play an important part, since there is much varietal difference – there is more to it than just the colours of the fruit!

So why the similarity of leaf but not of blossom in 'Warrior'? The most probable explanation is that one type is a seedling of the other, but which way round it is impossible to say, since two of the trees I have seen – one of each type – are extremely old, and indeed one tree has ceased to exist above ground. However suckers from the roots are producing excellent true-to-type leaves and fruit. It appears the original tree was growing on its own roots.

One owner has one of each type in his orchard, and his wife has said that the apples are different. Another owner has told me that some 'Warrior' fruit keep longer than others.

Apples do not come true from seed, but a few do produce seedlings which so resemble the female parent that it requires very great expertise to tell them apart - 'Blenheim Orange' is the most famous example. A very well known Somerset nursery stocks the true 'Blenheim Orange'.

'Warrior' has in the past been a very popular apple in the Sturminster Newton area, in both orchards and cottage gardens, and although I have no information that it was used as a cider apple, it may well have been a good apple for drying. Country people of past generations knew all about drying fruit for winter use - apples, pears, plums, and apricots to name but four. I remember my own mother's dried apricot jam with special affection!

My purpose in researching 'Warrior', is one of conservation, since unless new 'Warrior's are propagated, the cultivar will become extinct, as so many others have country-wide. I appeal to anyone aware of the possible existence of a 'Warrior' to get in touch with me. Likewise anyone who wishes to grow a new one.

In due course, when I have propagated some new young trees, I will be submitting them to the Brogdale Horticultural Trust (see page 67), where the national collection of over 2,000 different apple cultivars are kept. The submitted trees are grown on, fruited, and the fruit compared with other fruit from the collection to ensure 'Warrior' is not already in existence under a prior name. If not, it would join the collection and become a recorded variety.

In closing, I wish to thank the following owners of 'Warrior' trees for allowing me to visit their gardens and orchards, and others who gave me invaluable help in my search: Mr and Mrs G Clacy; Mr E Clarke; Mr J Cluett; Mr S E Cluett; Mr J Cowley; Mr and Mrs J Elkins; Mr T Fox; Mr P Goddard; Mr C Score; Mr and Mrs P G Stephens; Mr and Mrs C S Wingate-Saul and my colleague Bob Sanders.

ADDENDUM

As requested, I submitted the proof of the above article on the 4 August 1993, less than five months after I was first introduced to 'Warrior', and had made my first graft on the 16 April. Thus I was not able to describe the mature fruit I later received, although in response to a further request from the Hon. Editor of The Society of Dorset Men, a drawing was quickly made and despatched to the printers.

The youngest of the five 'Warrior' trees I found is 63 years old (I met the farmer who had grafted it) and from this tree I was supplied with sufficient fruit for testing. The other four trees had become biennial and only bore just enough fruit to confirm that they are 'Warrior'.

The reason why 'Warrior' was once so popular was immediately apparent, for despite being an ugly misshapen apple it cooks to a froth and requires very little sugar - an egg-spoonful is enough for a baked apple or like amount of puree. I have sampled both, and find them acceptable when eaten raw as well. Certainly poor people in the last century would have prized 'Warrior' as sugar was not exactly a cheap commodity.

'Warrior' was exhibited at the RHS Fruit and Vegetable Committee in 1947 by W F Stockholm Esq of Uxbridge, a founder member of the RHS Fruit Group.

JOHN SALE is a keen amateur fruit grower, member of the RHS Fruit Group Committee and Chairman of the South-West Branch of the Group

Wisley's Model Gardens

JIM ARBURY

THE MODEL FRUIT Gardens are one of the most popular areas at Wisley attracting many visitors throughout the year. There is always something of interest to see, whether flowers, fruit or just the forms of trees themselves. The fruit gardens occupy an area of approximately a third of an acre enclosed by a hornbeam *(Carpinus betulus)* hedge.

It was in 1947 that the first Model Fruit Gardens were planted at the request of the RHS Fruit Group to show amateur gardeners trees of restricted form that are suitable for planting in a small area and also how a fruit garden can be planned where space is limited. Although the objectives have changed very little over the years, the gardens themselves have altered considerably. Originally the three gardens measured 14.5 x 27.5m (48 x 90ft), 14.5 x 18m (48 x 60ft) and 9 x 18m (30 x 60ft); sizes which were considered suitable for inclusion in, respectively, a large, medium and small private garden. Since then the average size of private gardens

has diminished and the model gardens have been reduced accordingly. There are now gardens 14.5 x 18m (48 x 60ft), 9 x 18m (30 x 60ft), 9 x 9m (30 x 30ft) and two 9 x 5m (30 x 17ft) and of these the smallest sized gardens attract particular attention from visitors.

All the gardens are planted with a wide range of fruits to provide fruit for most of the year. For example, the south-facing 9 x 5m (30 x 17ft) garden contains cordon gooseberries and red and whitecurrants, blackcurrants, summer and autumn-fruiting raspberries, cordon apples and pears, fan-trained peaches, a Tayberry and a Tummelberry trained over an arch.

The Model Fruit Gardens at Wisley, first planted in 1947

The large 14.5 x 8m (48 x 60ft) garden was, until 1993, enclosed by a large timber-framed fruit cage. This cage was removed when the structure began to rot. There are now plans to design a replacement garden. The proposed new garden will include a wall and a patio area. The walls will be used to demonstrate fan-trained fruit while the glasshouse and patio will give prominence to the cultivation of fruit in containers. There will also be a fruit tunnel of cordon apples and various trained forms of trees.

GOOSEBERRY, RED- AND WHITECURRANT COLLECTIONS

The gooseberry collection was replanted in 1986 and expanded to include around 100 cultivars grown as cordons. This is a form particularly suited for small gardens and also enables the collection to be contained in a relatively small area.

Gooseberries are an excellent garden fruit with a long season of use if a range of cultivars are grown. Many of the fine flavoured dessert gooseberries in the collection were bred in the 18th and 19th centuries in the north-west of England by members of gooseberry clubs. These include, 'Early Green Hairy', 'Golden Drop', 'Yellow Champagne', 'Red Champagne', 'Langley Gage' and 'Lord Derby'.

The red- and whitecurrant collection consists of around 30 cultivars, including oldies such as 'Raby Castle', 'Versailles Blanche' (syn. 'White Versailles'), 'Rivers' Late Red' and a pink currant, 'Champagne'. The latest large-berried cultivars, such as 'Jonkheer van Tets', 'Stanza' and 'Rovada', are also to be seen.

NEW IDEAS AND INTRODUCTIONS

The gardens are also important in demonstrating the latest fruit growing ideas and techniques using new cultivars and different rootstocks. Although some demonstrations are included throughout the Model Fruit Gardens, the west side in particular is devoted to these. Some tree forms included in this area have become very popular, such as apples grafted on the very dwarfing rootstock M27, the self-fertile sweet cherry 'Stella' and genetic dwarf compact peaches.

Kiwi fruit, *Actinidia deliciosa*, is grown and crops successfully, but it is essential to protect the young growth from spring frosts and cold winds. This is achieved by covering the plant with shade netting or spun polypropylene fleece. A smooth skinned relative with a better flavour, *A. arguta* is also grown. This is as frost tender as *A. deliciosa* but is less vigorous and the fruit ripens on the vine from late September onwards. As the fruit of *A. deliciosa* does not ripen fully on the vine it is harvested in late October and placed in the fruit store where ripening is speeded up by ethylene gas given off by ripening apples.

A small planting of the Arctic raspberry hybrid *Rubus arcticus* subsp. *stellarcticus,* has also attracted great interest. This low growing 15cm (38in) plant has attractive pink blossom and small red fruits which are popular in Scandinavia. The jam has a sharp aromatic flavour and is highly thought of in Sweden.

A demonstration of American highbush and half-high blueberries has proved very productive. Like rhododendrons they grow best in a soil with a pH of 4.0 to 5.5. The pH is kept low by using acidic mulches of well rotted pine needles or composted bark. The bushes are fairly trouble free, but the fruits must be netted against birds if any are to be harvested. Cultivars include 'Patriot', 'Bluetta', 'Goldtraube', 'Heerma' and 'Ivanhoe'.

DWARFING ROOTSTOCKS

Throughout the gardens great use is made of dwarfing rootstocks and compact forms of top fruit. We use the very dwarfing apple rootstock M27 extensively. One plot demonstrates its use both for spindlebushes and for horizontal cordons. Spindlebush trees have proved very productive and a suitable method for training trees on M27 as on this rootstock branches are not really strong enough to form a well-shaped bush tree.

Horizontal cordons popularly referred to as 'step overs' are in fact an old technique of training apples or pears as a low cordon about 45cm (18in) above ground level. This method was widely used in formal walled gardens in the past, particularly in France at Versailles in the Potager du Roi. (see p14 for an account of RHS Fruit Group visit). M27 has made 'step overs' easier to achieve and they make an attractive and productive border.

The dwarfing plum rootstock 'Pixy' is used for pyramids, fans and cordon-trained trees. Pyramid trees are suitable for small gardens and by using the technique of festooning - looping the branches down to reduce vigour and encourage fruiting - a small compact tree of 1.8m (6ft) can be achieved. All cultivars can be grown by this method, but compact cultivars particularly suited include 'Czar' and 'Blue Tit'. With 'Pixy' it is also possible to grow plums as oblique or upright cordons – not practicable with the more vigorous rootstocks.

PEST AND DISEASE CONTROL

The enclosed, sheltered areas in the gardens have warm microclimates useful for producing high quality fruit, but also providing ideal conditions for many pests and diseases. To control the various pests and diseases a comprehensive spray programme is used. Wherever possible the least toxic chemicals are used and cultural or biological control is also proving effective. Pheromone traps are used to trap male codling moths and monitor moth numbers. In addition, these pheromone traps indicate when pesticides should be applied to control this pest.

Cultural methods of disease control include the use of polythene covers as a means of preventing peach leaf curl (*Taphrina deformans*). This method was pioneered at Wisley and involves covering outdoor fan-trained peaches from December until the leaves have developed. In fact the covers are left on until mid to late May as a means of frost protection and to improve fruit set. This covering prevents the fungus developing and is now a widely used method of control.

Biological means of pest control include the use of the predatory mite *Phytoseiulus persimilis* to control the two-spotted spider mite (*Tetranychus urticae*) on peaches, strawberries and raspberries. Parasitic nematodes are introduced to control vine weevil (*Otiorhynchus sulcatus*) which has become a serious pest over the past few years. There are few effective ways of controlling vine weevil larvae and the use of nematodes seems to be the only realistic method.

INTEGRATED PEST AND DISEASE CONTROL

A recently planted plot in the gardens demonstrates the cultivation of fruit using a minimum of pesticides. Pest and disease resistant or tolerant cultivars of fruit have been selected wherever possible. Cultural and biological control methods have been used if appropriate. 1994 was only the second full season of this demonstration and therefore we still have much to learn about its successes or failures.

FEEDING, MANURING AND WATERING

The soil of the Model Fruit Gardens is naturally sandy, acidic and free draining. However, this poor soil has been improved greatly over the years with applications of mulch around the trees and bushes of rotted farmyard manure or spent mushroom compost. For raspberries composted bark is used, and for blueberries rotted pine needles or composted bark. Overall mulches of coarse bark are also used

A 1:1:2 NPK (6:6:12) fertilizer is applied in February with amounts varying with the crops. In addition, we also use sulphate of potash, sulphate of ammonia and calcium ammonium nitrate according to crop. If peaches and figs are carrying a heavy crop they receive supplementary liquid feeds of a high potash tomato fertilizer as the fruits develop.

Drip hoses and mini sprinklers are used for watering controlled by battery operated timers. This enables irrigation to be carried out at night when evaporation is lower than during the day. This irrigation system was installed by the Fruit Department staff in 1989 and has proved very successful, particularly during dry summers. Water is applied economically and the system is very labour saving.

LESSONS LEARNT

In the 47 years since the Model Fruit Gardens were established the designs and crops have changed and evolved, but the objectives remain the same. The gardens have clearly demonstrated how wide a range of fruits can be grown successfully in a small garden, from soft fruits to top fruits and including less hardy fruits such as peaches. We have also found out what will now grow well: apricots seldom produce much fruit and figs are only moderately successful.

Some cultivars have proved more successful than others. Interestingly, E G Gilbert, writing about the gardens in *The Journal of Royal of Horticultural Society*, September 1953, notes that the apple 'Sunset' had not done well, whereas 'Cox's Orange Pippin' had. Today 'Sunset' grows well which is probably due to the continual soil improvement over the intervening 40 years.

Although three bush apple trees on M7 and a row of cordon pears remain of the trees planted in 1947, the range of cultivars is kept as up-to-date as possible and the number continually increased.

JIM ARBURY is Fruit Technical Adviser at the RHS Garden Wisley

Scottish Soft Fruit Developments

RONNIE McNICOL

THE PERENNIAL NATURE of soft fruit crops makes their improvement through breeding a long term process. It can take 15 to 20 years from making the cross to releasing a new cultivar into commerce, and several further years before it trickles through to the amateur gardener.

Serious plant breeding, the deliberate crossing of selected parents to produce progeny from which superior genotypes (clones) could be identified, started around the late 19th and 20th centuries for the major soft fruit crops, strawberry, raspberry and blackcurrant. Until this time new cultivars had resulted from chance crossings. Plant breeding is a form of accelerated evolution and is an exercise in exploiting and manipulating the genetic system. Over the past 100 years or so, most of the important agricultural and horticultural crops have undergone many generations of deliberate selection and adaptation. Various studies have estimated that 50 per cent or more of the increase in agricultural production over the past 30 years has been due to better crop cultivars. The remaining increase being attributed to better pest and disease control and improvements in growing and post harvest handling practices.

I intend taking the liberty of using the past and ongoing soft fruit scientific programmes at SCRI (Scottish Crop Research Institute) to illustrate achievements to date and the future potential for the soft fruit crops that we work with. I should also emphasise at this stage that while much of the work of SCRI is 'high science', many aspects confer important spin-off advantages for the amateur gardener and of course to the ultimate user of the fruits of our labours, the consumer.

Tayside has been an important soft fruit growing region of the UK since the 1920s. It alone has accounted for about half of the UK raspberry production. In 1946 the Scottish Raspberry Investigation was formed with its base at the University College, Dundee, under the administration of East Malling Research Station in Kent, to study 'the disease causing the decline in yield and vigour of raspberries'. The findings of the investigation and their implementation led to the revival of the Scottish raspberry industry.

Following recommendations of the Horticultural Research Committee in 1951, Mylnefield Farm at Invergowrie, by Dundee, was identified and purchased as a site for a new horticultural research station called the Scottish Horticultural Research Institute (SHRI). Further changes took place in 1981 when the SHRI was amalgamated with the Scottish Plant Breeding Station to form the Scottish Crop Research Institute (SCRI).

SCRI is the lead centre in the UK for research on soft fruit (raspberries, blackberries, blackcurrants and strawberries), barley and potatoes. SCRI operates as a truly interdisciplinary research group and my colleagues, who are virologists, nematologists, entomologists, plant physiologists, agronomists, bacteriologists, biotechnologists, statisticians, chemists and fellow geneticists, all contribute either directly by screening material or in providing advice and guidance from their specialised knowledge. It is this interactive nature of the scientists at SCRI and their extensive knowledge base that enables us to have one of the most internationally successful soft fruit breeding programmes. This success can be evaluated by looking at the uptake of SCRI cultivars both within the UK and on an international scale.

Our raspberry cultivars 'Glen Clova' (released 1969), 'Glen Moy' and 'Glen Prosen' (both released in 1981) occupy in excess of 90 per cent of the Scottish area and more than 70 per cent of the certified healthy raspberry cane production in the UK. They are also grown commercially in Germany, Denmark, France, Spain, Australia, New Zealand, Chile and Argentina. The hybridberries (red raspberry x blackberry hybrids) Tayberry and Tummelberry and the SCRI spine-free blackberry 'Loch Ness' are all grown throughout the world. SCRI blackcurrant cultivars are planted on about 80 per cent of the UK hectarage and are of major importance in most countries with a significant blackcurrant industry, including New Zealand, Poland, Scandinavia and Canada. Even with strawberries, which are much more environmentally sensitive than the other soft fruit crops, our cultivar 'Melody' has performed well in Poland and we have released a seedling in Australia. So the belief held by some, that SCRI breeds new soft fruit cultivars for Scotland, while in fact true, is very far from being the whole story!

NEW RASPBERRIES

The Institute's first success in raspberry breeding was 'Glen Clova', which, when released in 1969, outyielded existing cultivars by some 25 to 30 per cent. It is a vigorous cultivar which ripens early and produces medium-sized, light to medium-coloured fruit which are excellent for canning and freezing.

'Glen Moy' is an early cultivar, like 'Glen Clova', and was released in 1981. It is however, spineless, which minimises damage to the fruit and has a better yield, fruit size and flavour. It is resistant to the main aphid vector of virus diseases but is susceptible to raspberry midge, blight and raspberry root rot. Despite these failings 'Glen Moy' is now established as the best early cultivar, and is very popular with both supermarkets and Pick-Your-Own growers for its large berries of medium red colour.

'Glen Prosen' (released 1981) is a late mid-season cultivar, but like 'Glen Moy' has moderate vigour and spine-free canes. Fruits are exceptionally firm which confers a degree of resistance to grey mould and makes it useful in wet seasons and for transport to distant markets, or for freezing or canning. The fruit is slightly larger than 'Glen Clova', medium red in colour and easily removed from the plug.

'Glen Garry' (released 1990) and 'Glen Lyon' (released 1991) are the most recent raspberry releases of generally available plants. The former has very large fruit because it has gene L_1. This increases fruit size by prolonging the growth of the receptacle so that it bears more drupelets of larger individual size. 'Glen Garry' is the first cultivar to have this L_1 gene and the first to give fruit which typically average 5-6gm (Jennings & McNicol 1991). 'Glen Garry' is early ripening, produces pale fruit of firmer texture than 'Malling Delight', from which it is derived, and has a good flavour.

'Glen Lyon' is also spine-free and produces canes of moderate height. The slow growth of new canes results in fruit that is well presented to the pickers. The fruit are also extremely bright making 'Glen Lyon' very attractive and ideally suited to the fresh market with low sugar content and high acidity. Test marketing has proved it to be highly acceptable to consumers who like the bright colour, firm texture and frequently mix the fruit with something sweeter.

Four new raspberries have just been released and, with one exception, there are unlikely to be quantities of plant material generally available for 2 to 3 years. They have been called the Glen M.A.R.S. series for 'Glen Magna', 'Glen Rosa' and 'Glen Shee', and they cover a spread of season and a variety of uses. The late season, 'Glen Magna', is aimed primarily at the Pick-Your-Own and ama-

teur markets as a potential replacement for 'Leo'. The canes are vigorous, upright, and have a few spines, but it is the size and flavour of the fruit that is startling. The large, dark, conical fruit commonly weigh 6 gm with individual fruit of over 9 gm being recorded. In comparison, 'Glen Clova' will only average fruit of about 2 to 5 gm throughout a season. Plants of 'Glen Magna' are specifically being propagated using the latest tissue culture techniques in order to make limited quantities available to the amateur trade within the next 12 months.

HYBRID FRUITS

The Tayberry is a hybrid of the blackberry cultivar 'Aurora', from Oregon, and an unnamed raspberry bred at the SCRI. It is therefore the same kind of hybrid as the loganberry, which was produced 100 years ago by crossing a Californian blackberry and a raspberry. The Tayberry shows improvements over the loganberry, especially in fruit size, because the bigger blackberries and raspberries now available have proved better parents than the cultivars then available to Judge Logan.

Tayberry fruit is about 4 cm ($1\frac{1}{2}$in) long, deep purple in colour, and, like the loganberry, has inherited the rich flavour typical of the blackberries found in western America. Its core is retained in the fruit when picked, like the blackberry. The first fruit ripen about the same time as a mid-season raspberry, but the hybrid has a longer ripening season than raspberries. Hence it is ideal for filling the gap in production between late raspberries and early blackberries. The fruit is excellent for eating fresh, for freezing and for making jam or wine. Unfortunately, the plant is very thorny and has a spreading growth habit with cultural requirements similar to those of blackberries and loganberries. In trials it has yielded 12.5 tonnes per hectare (5.1 tonnes per acre) but, in commercial practice, maximum yields of 7.5 tonnes are more likely.

The Tummelberry is a new hybrid fruit obtained by crossing the Tayberry with one of its sister hybrids. It was released because some consumers prefer the sharper and less aromatic flavour. Compared with the Tayberry its fruit are rounder and redder; they also begin ripening about five days later. Tummelberry canes are slightly more erect and hardy than those of Tayberry; consequently it may yield more when winter injury is a problem, but otherwise it gives a similar or slightly lower yield.

'Glencoe' is a purple raspberry which was bred by first tranferring the recessive gene *s*, for spinelessness, from a red raspberry to a black raspberry and then using the spine-free black raspberry to produce purple hybrids by backcrossing to red raspberry. It has an intense flavour and colour and is particularly suitable for products such as yoghurt, juice, flavourings and seedless jam. Fruit set can be a problem with diploid purple raspberries like 'Glencoe' and most of our breeding of purples is now taking place at the tetraploid level which improves fertility and increases fruit size (Jennings & McNicol, 1989).

BLACKBERRIES

In 1966 attempts were made to breed blackberries for northern Britain at SCRI. The aim was to combine the erect and early flowering habit of 'Darrow', the spinelessnesss of 'Thornfree' and the rapid fruit maturation of 'Chehalem' or 'Ashton Cross'. The programme required several generations of breeding before the first European bred, spine-free blackberry could be released which has been named 'Loch Ness'. While 'Loch Ness' (released 1988) is a significant improvement on previous blackberries in terms of yield and winter hardiness, it does not realise its full cropping potential in Scotland because it is still not sufficiently early ripening. However, the most recent SCRI selection to be sent for trialling are capable of almost finishing their crop before 'Loch Ness' is in full pick. These genotypes will therefore be complementary in season. The latest selections are larger fruited, firmer fleshed and of better flavour than 'Loch Ness' and should prove suitable for mountain and northern areas of Europe.

BLACKCURRANTS

The SCRI blackcurrant programme is funded by SmithKline Beecham Blackcurrant Research and Development Fund and has produced the 'Ben' series of cultivars that now dominate the UK due mainly to their high yields and frost tolerance during the flowering period. Again, pest resistance has become a high breeding priority, particularly in the case of gall mite and leaf curling midge which both require extensive chemical control measures. Losses due to gall mite infestation and subsequent infection with reversion have increased in recent years. The need for resistant cultivars is urgent and the SCRI programme is using mite-resistant genes from gooseberries and other fruits.

However, objectives like frost tolerance and cropping consistency continue to be a high priority. By examining the mechanisms of frost tolerance in our scientific programmes we can now breed more effectively for this character.

Blackcurrant in the UK is almost entirely used for juice processing. However, our newest cultivar, 'Ben Connan', is aimed specifically at the non-processing Pick-Your-Own and amateur markets. It produces exceptionally high yields of very large fruit on a plant with compact growth characteristics. In addition to good resistance to powdery mildew, 'Ben Connan' has shown strong resistance to leaf-curling midge.

STRAWBERRIES

The strawberry programme at SCRI is concentrated mainly on producing disease resistant (mainly to red core) fresh fruit cultivars. The cultivar 'Symphony' has just been released to the commercial and amateur markets. It is a late mid-season type with a 50 per cent picking date 8 to 10 days later than 'Elsanta', making it an ideal follow on. The fruit are well suited to the fresh market since they are glossy, uniform in shape, firm and have an excellent sweet flavour. Again, as with our other fruit crops, we place a very high priority on flavour and consistency of cropping under a wide range of environmental conditions with a minimum of pesticide input.

THE FUTURE

Breeding perennial soft fruit crops is essentially a long term process and techniques are now becoming available that allow us to speed up the release of new cultivars. One such technique is tissue culture whereby plants of the new culti-

vars are multiplied up very rapidly in glass or plastic ware under laboratory conditions. This permits, maybe, a million daughter plants to be produced from one mother plant in place of about 25 that are produced through conventional procedures. Such techniques are being used commercially to release all our new fruit cultivars and this has enabled small quantities of 'Symphony' and 'Glen Magna' to be made available to the public within a year of release, a process that previously would have taken several years.

At SCRI we have taken this process a stage further and have pioneered new tissue culture techniques for raspberry (McNicol & Graham, 1990) - and incidentally blackcurrant, strawberry and blueberry - which allow the regeneration of whole plants from virtually a single cell and also gene transfer techniques which allow us to insert potentially beneficial genes from other species and even other genera into our already highly adapted and commercially successful cultivars (Graham *et al.*, 1990). Already, the cowpea protease inhibitor gene (provided by Agricultural Genetics Company, Cambridge) which controls the production of an insect antimetabolite effective against a range of insect pests has been inserted into strawberry at SCRI. The effectiveness of this gene is now being tested under conditions outside the laboratory.

Much of our present work involves developing improved and more efficient breeding techniques that will reduce the time from initial cross to commercial release of improved cultivars. These cultivars will be able to crop effectively under environmentally sensitive, low input systems of production.

REFERENCES
GRAHAM, J, MCNICOL, R J & KUMAR, A (1990). Use of the GUS gene as a selectable marker for *Agrobacterium*-mediated transformation of *Rubus*. *Plant Cell, Tissue and Organ Culture* **20**, 35-39.

JENNINGS, D L & MCNICOL, R J (1989). Black raspberries and purple raspberries should be spine-free and tetraploid. *Acta Horticulturae* **262**, 89-92.

JENNINGS, D L & MCNICOL, R J (1991). *Rubus* breeding - recent progress and problems. *Plant Breeding Abstracts* **61**, 753-758.

MCNICOL, R J & GRAHAM, J (1990). *In vitro* regeneration of *Rubus* from leaf stem segments. *Plant Cell, Tissue and Organ Culture* **21**, 45-50.

RONNIE MCNICOL is the head of the Soft Fruit Genetics Department at SCRI.

Primocane Fruiting Raspberries

VICTORIA KNIGHT

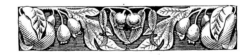

IN THE last 10 years interest in primocane fruiting raspberries has increased considerably. Most raspberries are biennial with fruit produced on the second year's growth (floricanes) in the summer. The terminal and axillary buds formed on the first year, or primocanes, initiate flower buds in the autumn and, following winter chilling, produce fruiting laterals in the second year. After fruiting, the whole cane dies back to the base and is cut out in the autumn.

In primocane fruiting cultivars, the terminal and some axillary buds develop flowers in the first year. The portion of the cane which fruited then dies back and only the lower portion bears a crop the following summer (Keep, 1988; Knight, 1987). Cultivars which produced a few fruit in September and October were known as autumn-fruiting, tip-fruiting, fall-bearing or everbearing, but newer cultivars, which produce more fruit earlier in the season, were more accurately described as primocane fruiting by Lawrence (1981) and this term is now being used universally.

The main advantages of primocane raspberries for the amateur grower are: extending the season from mid-August until the first frost; much simplified pruning; minimum support systems; shorter canes, which can be accommodated within a fruit cage; and less carry over of pests and diseases. The main disadvantages are: the picking commitment (at frequent intervals for 8 to 12 weeks); lower total yield; lower yield per pick and possible crop loss in a very wet and windy autumn.

The UK market price is generally lowest in July and increases from mid August onwards, although the price can fall if inclement weather adversely affects fruit quality. Primocane raspberries are almost twice as expensive to pick as summer fruiters, because less fruit is picked per day over a much longer period (Keep, 1988). Nevertheless, in recent years, some growers have made a profit on their primocane raspberries but a loss on their summer crop.

Establishment costs are much lower with primocane raspberries because they can be supported with stakes and string, rather than the full post and wire support system needed for biennial raspberries. Selective pruning and tying in summer fruiters is an extremely labour intensive operation, compared to the annual mowing of primocane fruiters. Over-wintering cane diseases are not a problem but commercial growers still need to spray to control fruit rots and raspberry beetle, and amateurs may need to control the beetle.

Raspberry beetle (*Byturus tomentosus*) usually produces two generations each year and lays eggs in the flowers on summer fruiters in May and June. If summer and primocane fruiters are growing in close proximity, the beetles can continue laying eggs in the open flowers on the primocanes in July and August. Therefore, primocane fruit that ripens in August and September can be infected with beetle larvae, but one spray at first pink fruit should give reasonable control. Unfortunately, because of their extended flowering season, first pink fruit will coincide with open flowers on other canes and sprays must be applied carefully to minimise the risks to bees.

BREEDING PRIMOCANE FRUITING CULTIVARS

There are breeding programmes aiming to produce new, improved cultivars of primocane raspberries in Europe, North America and Australia. The increased emphasis given to primocane types is reflected in the number of cultivars which have been introduced recently. Table 1 lists those released since 1983, starting with 'Autumn Bliss' from East Malling Research Station, now part of Horticulture Research International (HRI).

England

'Autumn Bliss' was such an improvement over 'Heritage', 'September' and 'Zeva Herbsternte' that it was taken up very quickly and primocane raspberry production in England changed from being a very small specialised operation to a natural extension of the summer crop. HRI East Malling has released three more primocane cultivars since 'Autumn Bliss'; 'Autumn Britten', a sib of 'Autumn Bliss' and trialled as 3676/6, performed well in trials in Canada and is being propagated for release by the Ontario Berry Growers Association. Fruit size, shape and colour of 'Autumn Britten' was sometimes better than that of 'Autumn Bliss', but in England 'Autumn Britten' was difficult to plug. In Ontario plugging has not been too much of a problem and they prefer to

Table 1: Primocane fruiting raspberries introduced since 1983

Cultivar	Parentage	Introduced	Raised in
'Autumn Bliss'	ex *Rubus arcticus*, *R. idaeus* *R. occidentalis* and 'Lloyd George'	1983	England
'Amity'	ex *R. idaeus strigosus*, *R. occidentalis*, 'Fallred' and 'Heritage'	1984	Oregon
'Fallbrook'	Open-pollinated seedlings from New Hampshire	1984	Alberta
'Perrons Red'	'Zeva Herbsternte' x 'Pathfinder'	1987	Quebec
'Joe Mello'	Reiter 323 x 'Chilcotin'	1988	California
'Redwing'	'Heritage' x 'Fallred'	1988	Minnesota
'Summit'	ex 'Fallred', New York selection, 'Newburgh','Washington' and 'Willamette'	1989	Oregon
'Sweetbriar'		1990	California
'Ruby'	'Titan' x New York hybrid	1990	New York
'Autumn Cascade'	ex *R. arcticus*, *R. idaeus strigosus*, *R. occidentalis*, *R. odoratus*, 'Lloyd George' and 'Zeva Herbsternte'	1990	England
'Polana'	'Heritage' x 'Zeva Herbsternte'	1991	Poland
'Dinkum'	'Autumn Bliss' x 'Glen Moy'	1992	Victoria
'Allgold'	Yellow-fruited sport of 'Autumn Bliss'	1992	England
'Autumn Britten'	Sib of 'Autumn Bliss' same parentage	1993	England
'Autumn Cygnet'	Sib of 'Autumn Cascade' same parentage	1993	England
'Red River'	('Fallred' x *R. idaeus strigosus* selection) x ('Fallred' x 'Boyne')	1993	Manitoba
'Bogong'	'Comox' x 'Autumn Bliss'	1994	Victoria
'Joan Squire'	Two complex hybrids	1994	England
'Goldie'	Yellow-fruited sport of 'Heritage'	1994	California
'Kiwigold'	Yellow-fruited sport of 'Heritage'	1994	New Zealand
'Terri-Louise'	'Autumn Bliss' x 'Glen Moy'	1994	England

use the newer 'Autumn Britten'.

'Autumn Cascade' is a moderately high-yielding, early-ripening, self-supporting, spineless primocane cultivar (trialled as 4395/65), which was taken up by Specialist Fruit Plants Ltd in 1990 under license from HRI to exploit the cultivar in England, France, Portugal, Switzerland and Hungary. 'Autumn Cascade' plugs more readily than 'Autumn Bliss' and there is interest in harvesting it by machine. It has also performed well in southern France and Portugal, where other cultivars suffered from sun scald. 'Autumn Cygnet' (4395/75) is a sib of 'Autumn Cascade' which did well in Tasmania and is being propagated for sale in Australia by Tasmanian Berry Gardens.

These three introductions illustrate the international market for primocane cultivars. Many summer-fruiting raspberries are locally adapted and do best in the country of origin. In contrast, 'Heritage' released from New York State in 1969, is widely adapted and grown in North and South America, Europe and Australasia (Daubeny *et al.*, 1992). 'Heritage' is the main cultivar seen on the market in the northern Hemisphere in winter and its ability to travel well is due to several factors including firm texture, non-darkening colour and good shelf life. 'Autumn Bliss' grows well in many countries but is too soft for intercontinental shipping. However it has had a huge impact as a parent in all primocane breeding programmes, as a donor of earliness, high yield, large fruit and resistance to *Phytophthora* root rot.

The main objectives of the HRI primocane programme are increased yields of larger, better quality fruit; easy plugging; better shelf life; more condensed ripening in both early-ripening and mid-season types; sturdy self-supporting canes; spinelessness and resistance to the aphid virus vector *Amphorophora idaei*, raspberry beetle and *Phytophthora* root rot. Six HRI selections with different combinations of some of these characteristics were planted in Raspberry Primocane Trial 4 at the Brogdale Horticultural Trust in autumn 1994. 'Polana', 'Dinkum', 'Bogong', 'Joan Squire' and 'Terri-Louise' are also included in this trial.

There is minor interest in yellow-fruited raspberries for specialist outlets, in mixed packs with red raspberries and for the amateur market. Yellow fruit is recessive to red fruit and several red-fruited cultivars and breeding lines are heterozygous for this gene and give rise to a proportion of yellow-fruited seedlings in some progeny. Also, the gene for red fruit is unstable in some backgrounds and several yellow-fruited sports of 'Autumn Bliss' and 'Heritage' have been observed. Three of these, 'Allgold', 'Goldie' and 'Kiwigold' have been selected and introduced as cultivars in their own right.

Yellow-fruited primocane types tend to have soft fruit, and both the texture and colour deteriorate rapidly after picking. Since 1989, yellow-fruited HRI selections have been intercrossed to produce all-yellow progenies with improved fruit quality, especially texture and flavour. Derivatives of an earlier 'Summit' x 'Autumn Cascade' cross were segregated for red, yellow and an attractive apricot-coloured fruit. Two yellow and two apricot-fruited HRI selections have been planted in a small trial at Brogdale, along with 'Allgold' and 'Kiwigold'.

Government funding for plant breeding has declined in the last 10 years, and most programmes are now funded by a combination of public and grower money. Because of the longevity of plantations and the cane density per hectare, annual sales of raspberry canes and thus income from royalties is limited. Nevertheless, private breeders are interested in primocane raspberries and Medway Fruits are marketing 'Dinkum' from Australia in conjunction with Commercial Fruit Plants Ltd, and have also named 'Joan Squire' and 'Terri-Louise', bred by Dr Jennings, in 1994.

Continental Europe

The Research Institute of Pomology and Floriculture programme at Brzezna, Poland, released 'Polana' in 1991 (Danek, 1989). It is a mid-season primocane cultivar which ripens approximately two weeks after 'Autumn Bliss'. The fruits are a dark but bright red, large, with rather an uneven shape and slightly soft with a moderate flavour and poor shelf life.

Since 1980, the Institute of Horticultural Plant Breeding – Bälsgard, Sweden, has been breeding and selecting for early ripening primocane fruiting types (Trajkovski and Sjostedt, 1992). Much of their useful starting material was open-pollinated seed of HRI primocane fruiting selections, including 'Autumn Bliss' and 'Autumn Britten'. Following one or two further open-pollinated generations two selections, BRu8302-7 and BRu8802-1, are going ahead.

Häberli Obst-und Beerenzentrum AG, a private nursery company in Switzerland, have their own successful soft fruit breeding programmes. The main objective for raspberries is breeding for resistance to *Phytophthora* root rot, and 'Autumn Bliss' has been used as a donor of resistance (Spiegler and Thoss, 1993).

North America

North America covers a very wide range of climatic conditions, including extremely low winter temperatures, and biennial raspberries need winter hardiness to survive. Primocane cultivars avoid the problem of winter injury, but rapid growth in the sping and early ripening are required to maximise yield before the first frost. Four cultivars have been bred in regions with very cold winters 'Falbrook', 'Perrons Red', 'Redwing' and 'Red River', but only 'Redwing' has been trialled in the UK; 'Red River' will fruit at East Malling in 1995. 'Redwing' was poor compared to 'Autumn Bliss' in Primocane Trial 3 at Brogdale (low yield, small fruit), and it is unlikely that the other three will be well adapted to European conditions.

Cultivars bred in New York and Oregon are more likely to perform well here, but 'Amity' and 'Ruby' were disappointing at East Malling. 'Amity' ripened 3 to 4 weeks later than 'Autumn Bliss' but had a low yield of dark but firm fruit. 'Ruby' was similar to 'Heritage' in season and habit, but was exceptionally spiny and the fruit was of poor shape and difficult to plug.

'Joe Mello' and 'Sweetbriar' were bred by Sweetbriar Development Inc, Watsonville, California and although widely grown in California, they are not available to other breeders or growers. Primocane fruiting is important in California, where insufficient winter chilling reduces the yield of some of the summer fruiting cultivars (Fear and Meyer, 1993).

Australia

Lack of winter chilling was largely responsible for the poor performance of most summer-fruiting cultivars introduced into Australia from Europe and North America. The breeding programme in Victoria is therefore concentrating on climatic adaptation and extending the season, including primocane fruiting (McGregor, 1993). Two primocane cultivars have been released, both of which are derived from 'Autumn Bliss'. 'Dinkum' is similar to 'Autumn Bliss' in terms of yield, growth habit and fruit size, and is approximately one week later (Jennings, 1992). It plugs more readily than 'Autumn Bliss' and the fruit is slightly firmer and more cohesive, but it is more susceptible to root rot. 'Bogong' starts off the season with very large, attractive fruit, but quality deteriorates; it is considerably later than 'Autumn Bliss'.

CHANGES IN RASPBERRY PRODUCTION

The introduction of higher yielding, earlier ripening primocane varieties has resulted in great changes in raspberry production worldwide. In the traditional raspberry growing areas early primocane cultivars have extended the season by 10 to 12 weeks, which has improved returns for growers and increased sales of fresh fruit. In areas with hot, dry summers and mild winters, primocane raspberries avoid the problem of insufficient winter chilling and allow fruit production to miss the peak summer temperatures. At the other extreme, primocane raspberries can be grown where insufficient winter hardiness of summer-fruiting types is a limiting factor.

In a very short time, raspberries have changed from a short season, local crop to a worldwide commodity available for nearly 50 weeks of the year. Chile has the fastest rising acreage and is exporting raspberries to North America and Europe from December to April. The Republic of South Africa and Zimbabwe see raspberries as having great potential.

Areas in southern Europe are interested in diversifying, and small experimental areas of primocane raspberries have been planted in Greece, Portugal, Spain and southern Italy, with the aim of producing fruit from November to March for export to northern Europe. The CEC is funding research in this area as a means of increasing farm income in southern Europe and reducing imports from outside the Community. Among cane fruit crops, the primocane fruiting character is expressed strongly only in raspberries and another aspect of the CEC-funded project is to transfer this character to loganberry types and blackberries.

SUMMARY

Primocane fruiting raspberries released from public and privately funded breeding programmes in the last few years have dramatically changed raspberry production. European markets trade in fresh raspberries throughout the year, from an increasing number of sources in both the northern and southern hemispheres, and amateur growers can produce their own fresh fruit for four months without protection.

Many cultivars have been released

recently and are still relatively unknown, but some can be seen in the fruit garden at Wisley. 'Autumn Bliss' is still highly recommended for amateurs but there are several new, improved primocane types being considered for release and breeders are striving to produce even better cultivars for the next century.

REFERENCES

DANEK, J, 1989. Raspberry breeding in Poland. *Acta Horticulturae,* **262**, 57-60.

DAUBENY, H A, MALONEY, K and McGREGOR, G R, 1992. 'Heritage' red raspberry. *Fruit Varieties Journal,* **46**, 2-3.

FEAR, C D and MEYER, M L, 1993. Breeding and variation in *Rubus* germplasm for low winter chill requirement. *Acta Horticulturae,* **352**, 295-303.

JENNINGS, D L, 1992. Dinkum weathers the autumn storms. *The Fruit Grower,* November 1992, 21-22.

KEEP, E, 1988. Primocane (autumn)-fruiting raspberries: a review with particular reference to progress in breeding. *Journal of Horticultural Science,* **63**, 1-18.

KNIGHT, V H, 1987. Breeding autumn-fruiting raspberries. *The Garden,* **112**, 318-322.

LAWRENCE, F J, 1981. Another look at 'day neutral' strawberries and 'primocane fruiting' raspberries. *Annual Report Oregon Horticultural Society,* **72**, 108-113.

McGREGOR, G R, 1993. Progress in raspberry breeding for southern Australia. *Acta Horticuturae,* **352**, 381-386.

SPIEGLER, G and THOSS, H, 1993. Breeding for resistance to *Phytophthora* root rot in red raspberries. *Acta Horticulturae,* **352**, 477-484.

TRAJKOVSKI, V and SJOSTEDT, B, 1992. Raspberry breeding. *Bälsgard Institute of Horticultural Plant Breeding Report 1990-1,* 46-51.

VICTORIA KNIGHT is the Raspberry Breeder in the Breeding and Genetics Department at HRI. She has been breeding Ribes *and* Rubus *species since 1972, specialising*

Growing Strawberries on Raised Beds

SHEILA BAXTER

THERE ARE SEVERAL advantages to growing strawberries on raised beds:

• It provides a greater depth of drained soil for the plants, which reduces the risk of red core and crown rot diseases in wet winters.

• Fruit is less likely to lie in water and rot on a raised bed.

* It is easier to pick the fruit from a raised bed.

* Fruiting is often earlier.

Commercially, the beds are made at 1.5m (5ft) centres by ploughing a double furrow into the middle of the bed from each side, after subsoiling down the centre line to ensure good drainage. This leaves a rounded bed with a flat top, about 1m (3ft) wide and 20cm (8 in) high, on which two rows of strawberries are planted.

The flat top of the bed allows rain to penetrate the soil when a polythene mulch is not used. If it is ridged up sharply, as for potatoes, the rain simply runs off the sides into the gulleys between the rows. For the gardener this means hard labour with the spade! However, there is no reason why a single row bed of half the width should not be used, except that it is a less economical use of space, since the alleys between the beds are about 50cm (20in) wide whether the beds are for single or double rows.

When making beds, it is very important to ensure that the soil is in the right condition, that is, friable and neither very wet nor very dry. Either of these extreme conditions will lead to problems of soil consolidation and poor plant growth in the future.

USING A POLYTHENE MULCH
A polythene mulch serves several purposes:

* It is a good way of controlling weeds in the rows.

* Black and coloured polythene warms

the soil in the spring which promotes earlier cropping.

* It helps to retain moisture and reduces evaporation so that soil can be prepared and maintained in the right condition.

* Less straw is needed where a polythene mulch is used.

* Runners cannot root in the rows.

There are certain disadvantages, however.

* Planting holes in a polythene mulch have to be hand weeded until the plants have filled the holes, as herbicides cannot be used.

* Careful cutting of runners is needed where polythene is used.

* Irrigation is essential under a polythene mulch

* A black polythene mulch can cook the fruit in very hot weather.

* A polythene mulch is an ideal habitat for the vine weevil, which can devastate the crop.

For a normal two-row bed, 1.3m (4ft 3in) wide, 150 gauge black polythene is usually used. If the summer is very hot, a wisp of straw is added along the sides of the polythene, as well as the normal layer of straw in the alleys, to prevent the fruit cooking on the polythene. Where cold-stored plants, which produce fruit in 60 days, are grown to crop during the heat of summer, a white-on-black polythene is used with the white side uppermost to reflect the heat.

Before the polythene is laid, an irrigation pipe, such as T-tape or the longer lasting Leaky Pipe, must be installed. Normally a single line is laid down the centre of the bed, but now that the nematode *Steinernema carpocase* is used to control vine weevil, two lines will be necessary, either beside or under each row so that the nematode can be irrigated down the pipes and reach its prey. The irrigation pipe can also be used to apply liquid fertilizer to the strawberries and a tomato feed gives good results. This is particularly important for everbearer cultivars which need much more feeding than summer-fruiting ones. The latter should only be fed from the second year onwards, assuming that a base fertilizer has been applied before planting.

LAYING DOWN THE POLYTHENE

It is essential to lay the polythene so that it is tight against the soil, or it will blow about and tear and weeds will grow under it. This is relatively easy with commercial machinery designed for the job, but for the gardener it has to be done with a spade.

Start by marking 1m (3ft) across each end of the bed, then peg a line down the length of the bed to the marks on one side. Starting at one end, make a slit in the soil using a spade facing you. Push it into the soil to about half its depth, then pull it towards you before removing it. This leaves a V-shaped slit with the soil pulled towards the alley. Continue doing this along the line on one side and repeat on the other. Next, dig a trench across each end of the bed.

When completed, lay the polythene on one end of the bed and unroll

enough of it to put the end down into the trench and up the other side. Refill the trench with soil and tread it in firmly. Unroll the rest of the polythene and repeat the process at the other end of the bed. The next job is to use the spade facing you again and gently push the polythene into the side slits so that it tightens over the soil. As you withdraw the spade, tread the soil tightly over and against the polythene to hold it firm.

If the polythene is not supplied with planting holes already in it, they

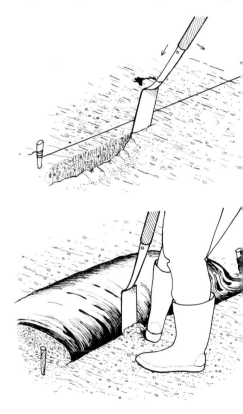

Top: push the spade down and forward to make a small V-shaped slit

Above: using the spade, gently push the edge of the polythene into the side slits and tread the soil firmly over it

can be made quite easily by using a 10cm (4in) diameter tin can with its lid removed and a hole made in the base into which the nozzle of a blowtorch can be fitted. A quick dab with the tin when the blowtorch is alight will made a clean hole in the polythene. Holes are usually made 30 to 35cm (12-14in) apart in two staggered rows, but for a very leafy cultivar such as 'Pandora', they may need to be nearer 40cm (16ih) apart.

Now all that has to be done is to plant the strawberries. This is an easy job if pot-grown plants are to be used, though the compost must be moist. Be careful if you are planting bare-root plants - this is where many people come

to grief. When planting long roots into a small hole, it is easy to plant them with their roots bent upwards, but this is the best way to stop them growing at all! If plants come with long roots, cut them off to about 15cm (6 in) long, so that they go straight down the planting hole. Also, do not plant them with a dibber, especially in wet or clay soils. The dibber can smooth the side of the hole and make it impossible for roots to get through into the soil beyond.

Finally, happy strawberry growing!

SHEILA BAXTER, a former member of the Ministry's Advisory Service (ADAS), is a member of the RHS Fruit Group Committee

Pest and Disease Management in Commercial Fruit Production

ANGELA BERRIE AND JERRY CROSS

MOST PEOPLE'S attitude to pesticides is founded on the belief that they are harmful to the environment and human health. Media attention about pesticide issues, such as contamination of water, residues in food and damage to wildlife and habitats, though sporadic is often intensive and almost invariably negative. This has led to increasing concern about the way in which food is pro-

duced. Fruit crops are subject to particular scrutiny because they are mostly consumed fresh and are considered, particularly in the case of apples, to symbolise healthy eating. However, despite these concerns, the considerable benefits of crop protection chemicals must not be overlooked. For the grower they provide an economic, easily managed, reliable growing system, allowing the production of high yields of quality fruit, with good shelf and storage life. For the consumer there has been a ready supply of cheap, good quality food. Despite these many advantages, the fruit industry has recognised the need to re-examine its approach to pest and disease control and to try to reduce its dependence on pesticides, not only to address the concerns of the consumer, but also to reduce costs in order to remain competitive with cheaper imports from Europe and elsewhere.

The industry recognises that organic production is not the answer. It is not feasible for fruit crops which are highly susceptible to pests and diseases. It would also be impossible to achieve the required yields and quality standards of the market place. 'Natural pesticides' advocated for organic production are insufficiently effective and, in any case, are not necessarily safer than synthetic pesticides.

However, pesticide use can be reduced in a number of ways. Alternative control methods, for example natural or biological control, resistant cultivars, cultural control, improved decision making so pesticides are only used when necessary, and improved spray application efficiency provide three options.

The best approach is to combine these three components into an integrated crop protection system. Biological, cultural, chemical and biotechnological control methods are combined with resistant cultivars, efficient crop monitoring, decision support systems and safe and effective spray application to minimise the use of pesticides. Integrated pest and disease management (IPDM) requires a high level of commitment from the grower with a clear understanding of the pest and disease complex of the crop and the range of control options available.

APPLES AND PEARS

PESTS: Unsprayed apple trees support a large and complex arthropod fauna amounting to more than one thousand species of insects and arachnids. Roughly 25 per cent are pests, 25 per cent natural enemies of pests and the remainder are neutral. About 20 of the pest species frequently cause significant fruit damage on unsprayed apple trees. They mostly attack the fruits directly and their natural enemies are not sufficiently effective to maintain populations below damaging levels. They are known as key pests (Table 1).

In commercial orchards key pests are controlled by a total of three or four sprays a year of moderately persistent, broad-spectrum insecticides such as chlorpyrifos and carbaryl. An insecticide spray is often needed before blossom to control aphids and caterpillars and/or at petal fall to control, in addition, capsids and sawfly. In summer one or two sprays are directed against codling and tortrix moths.

Use of broad-spectrum insecticides generally controls almost all the remaining minor pest species, but also greatly reduces numbers of natural enemies and neutral species. Most minor pests and natural enemies are eradicated which makes the key pests more troublesome, more prone to resurgence and hence more damaging.

Another crucial consequence is the emergence of secondary pests. These are not usually significant on unsprayed apple trees (mainly feeding on foliage),

Table 1: Main pests found in apple orchards

Pest	Common Name	Status	Importance
Aculus schlechtendali	Apple rust mite	Secondary	***
Adoxophes orana	Summer fruit tortrix moth	Secondary	***
Anthonomus pomorum	Apple blossom weevil	Key	*
Aphis pomi	Green apple aphid	Minor	*
Archips podana	Fruit tree tortrix moth	Secondary	**
Blastobasis decorella	Blastobasis caterpillar	Key	*
Cydia pomonella	Codling moth	Key	**
Dysaphis plantaginea	Rosy apple aphid	Key	***
Eriosoma lanigerum	Woolly aphid	Secondary	**
Forficula auricularia	Common earwig	Minor	*
Hoplocampa testudinea	Apple sawfly	Key	**
Lepidosaphes species	Mussel scale	Secondary	*
Leucoptera malifoliella	Apple leaf miner	Minor	-
Lygocoris pabulinus	Common green capsid	Key	**
Operophtera brumata	Winter moth	Key	**
Orthosia incerta	Clouded drab moth	Minor	*
Panonychus ulmi	Fruit tree red spider mite	Secondary	**
Rhopalosiphum insertum	Apple grass aphid	Minor	*

Key
-    rarely damaging
*   occasional damage
**   damage in most seasons
***   serious damage in most seasons

but in sprayed orchards have developed resistance to insecticides and build up to high populations where their natural enemies have been eradicated by broad-spectrum insecticides. The best known example is the fruit tree red spider mite. This emerged as a pest in the 1920s following the use of tar oil winter washes which were toxic to their natural enemies, the predatory Phytoseiid mites, but which had little effect on overwintering fruit tree red spider mite eggs. For several decades, this became the most important pest of apple and strains multi-resistant to insecticides and acaricides readily developed.

Another Phytophagous mite, the apple rust mite, also emerged as a secondary pest for the same reason. However, this was not recognised until the late 1970s when the acaricidal fungicides dinocap and binapacryl, used for mildew control and which effectively suppressed rust mite, were superseded by the triazole fungicides which were non acaricidal.

The whole situation on apple was transformed when the orchard predatory mite, *Typhlodromus pyri,* naturally developed resistance to most insecticides. Provided harmful pesticides (such as pyrethroid insecticides, pirimiphos-methyl, mancozeb) are not used, *T. pyri* regulates spider and rust mite numbers effectively so that acaricide use is not necessary. This system, known as integrated mite management, is now practised almost universally and has transformed pest management practices on apple completely.

Spider mites are not important pests of pears, but a similar development occurred with pear sucker which had become resistant to most broad-spectrum insecticides in the 1970s. Recognition of the importance of predatory flower bugs *(Anthocorid* species) as natural enemies of pear sucker, and avoidance of broad-spectrum insecticides in summer, has alleviated pear sucker problems, though sprays of selective insecticides are still needed.

There are several further secondary pests of apple and pear which still need attention. The most important is the summer fruit tortrix moth which is currently the most troublesome pest of apple and also important on pear. In Europe, it has been found that in unsprayed orchards high levels of parasitism by two or three species of parasitic wasp occur, but these are very susceptible to broad-spectrum pesticides. The next step towards comprehensive integrated pest managment is to tackle this pest. One strategy would be to find alternative control methods. Two main options are open: 1) juvenile hormone or ecdysone analogue insect growth regulators and 2) granulosis virus. The juvenile hormone insect growth regulator, fenoxycarb (Insegar) is highly active against summer fruit tortrix moth, and has transformed integrated pest management in most other European countries and become the mainstay of pest control programmes. Application against mature overwintered caterpillars eradicates the pest for several seasons and is also highly effective against codling moth and many other caterpillar pests.

Fenoxycarb is not approved for use in the UK. Work is in progress to obtain approval but this will take at least two years. It is only partially selective and it is possible that other pests (capsids, aphids and other sucking pests) will increase in importance as a result of its use. It is also dangerous to bees and therefore not a perfect solution. A better alternative may be the summer fruit tortrix moth granulosis virus which is available commercially in Switzerland. This is selective and has no undesirable side-effects. The main drawback is its high cost compared to conventional insecticides or fenoxycarb.

Another important component of integrated management is that pesticides should only be applied when necessary rather than routinely according to growth stage and calendar date. For apple pests, orchard monitoring systems have been well researched and thresholds of pest numbers for treatment decisions well established. A system of regular orchard monitoring, usually every two weeks, depending on growth stage and time of the season, has therefore been developed to determine when treatment is necessary. Inspections are visual with the aid of a hand lens and different parts of the tree (whole tree, blossoms, fruitlet clusters, leaves, shoots) are examined depending on the pest and time of the season. Such a monitoring schedule for apple is given in Table 3. In addition, pheromone traps are used to monitor important pests such as codling moth and other tortricids. Orchard monitoring is a vital part of IPDM and serves to determine need for treatment, time pesticide application for maximum effectiveness and evaluate the success of the treatments applied. Similar monitoring schedules have been developed for pears.

DISEASES

Apples and pears are also attacked by a complex of diseases including storage rots. Most sprays are directed at control of the scab and powdery mildew, both of which are serious diseases in unsprayed apple orchards. Unlike pests, although fungal hyperparasites or antagonists may be present, they do not serve to regulate disease incidence. This is more dependent on seasonal weather conditions and host or varietal susceptibility. Thus, in favourable seasons on susceptible apple trees, both scab and mildew can seriously reduce yield and fruit quality and weaken the tree. Disease control

therefore very much depends on using chemicals.

While pests can be monitored and treatment applied according to a threshold, the use of treatment thresholds for diseases, particularly scab, are not possible because considerably higher levels of disease may be present than are visible, such that damage has already occurred before treatment can be applied. Most growers therefore still rely on routine spray programmes from the start of growing to June, to achieve control, mainly because of the requirement for blemish-free fruit and because weather conditions in most years are favourable for apple scab (ie. wet).

The risk of apple scab attack can be determined by monitoring the weather: rainfall, leaf wetness, humidity and temperature. Recent research at HRI East Malling has resulted in the development of a new scab warning system (VENTEM™) with greater accuracy and reliability over previous systems. This warning system will soon be used by growers to target fungicide use according to the disease risk, thus improving disease control and reducing fungicide use. Similar systems are being developed for other fruit diseases such as apple canker and powdery mildew.

Disease monitoring, however, still plays an important part in integrated disease control. It provides a means of checking the success of fungicide treatments and allows modifications to be made where necessary. Powdery mildew, which does not damage fruit directly except at very high levels, can be monitored, and the amount of fungicide or number of sprays adjusted according to the disease pressure. Such a system is used commercially with considerable

Table 2: Main diseases found in apple orchards

Foliar / flower diseases

Venturia inaequalis – scab

Podosphaera leucotricha – mildew

Monilinia laxa f.sp. *mali* – blossom wilt

Fruit Diseases

Venturia inaequalis – scab

Botrytis cinerea – dry eye rot

Gloeodes pomigena – sooty blotch

Monilinia fructigena – brown rot

Bacterial diseases

Erwinia amylovora – fireblight

Pseudomonas syringae pv. *syringae* – bacterial blossom wilt

Canker and wood rots

Nectria galligena – canker

Chondrostereum purpureum – silver leaf

Diaporthe perniciosa – Diaporthe canker anthracnose and perennial canker

Root rots

Phytophthora cactorum – crown and collar rot

Pythium species – replant disease

Storage rots

Monilinia fructigena – brown rot

Nectria galligena – nectria rot
Gloeosporium species. – gloeosporium rot

Phytophthora syringae

Botrytis cinerea – botrytis rot

Penicillium expansum – blue mould

Mucor species.– Mucor rot

Botryosphaeria obtusa – rot

Diaporthe perniciosa – rot

Fusarium species – Fusarium rot

savings in fungicides. Cultural methods of control such as pruning out diseased tree parts, also offer possible ways of reducing fungicide use. Where possible such methods are incorporated into IPDM, but are usually labour intensive and costly on a commercial scale, although easily adopted in the garden.

Apples and pears are generally stored from September to March/April or longer in order to regulate the supply of fruit onto the market and compete with imported fruit. During storage they are subject to attack by a range of storage rots, which if not controlled, make storage uneconomic. Previously, rots were well controlled by the routine use of post-harvest fungicides which are the most environmentally and strategically sound means of rot control. With advances in research, integrated systems of control are being developed which incorporate cultural techniques and improved storage, such that post-harvest treatment need only be applied to fruit from orchards where a potential storage rot problem has been identified.

PLUMS AND CHERRIES

For cherries, pest problems are generally not serious because they are easily controlled by insecticides. Aphids and caterpillars can cause damage, but their levels are usually monitored and treatment applied if necessary, generally well before harvest. In contrast pest control on plums is dominated by control of the damson-hop aphid *(Phorodon humuli)* which has become resistant to almost all pesticides. This causes direct damage and also transmits the plum pox virus which reduces yield and fruit quality. The difficulties in controlling this aphid prevent further development of IPDM on plums. Spider and rust mites are also important because use of tar oil and pyrethroid insecticides to control the aphid have killed orchard predatory mites. Current research is directed at identifying effective natural enemies of the aphid.

On cherries and plums disease problems are few, but serious. Blossom wilt and brown rot diseases are prevalent in most seasons. Control relies on the use of fungicides at blossom time and two weeks pre-harvest combined with removal of overwintering cankers and mummified fruit. Routine sprays of copper fungicides are also applied post harvest to control bacterial canker.

SOFT FRUIT

Whereas IPDM programmes on top fruit are well established and used commercially, those in soft fruit are still in their infancy and require further research to improve and develop them. Nevertheless integrated methods of pest and disease control are employed.

Strawberries, though perennial, are short term in comparison to other fruit crops and are attacked by a wide range of damaging pests. One of the most important is the two spotted spider mite. Until the late 1980s, this pest was controlled with acaricides, but since the withdrawal of approval for cyhexatin, introduction of the predatory mite *Phytoseiulus persimilis* has became standard practice. Thus insecticides applied to control other pests, such as caterpillars, aphids and capsids, must be compatible with these predators.

Control of strawberry diseases, whether soil-borne (red core) or airborne *(Botrytis cinerea* and powdery mildew), requires an integrated approach combining cultural control, such as removal of crop debris, with the use of fungicides to achieve effective control. For soil-borne diseases such as verticillium wilt, resistant strawberry cultivars are available and are used in some production systems such as Pick-Your-Own. However, commercial production is focused currently on the cultivar 'Elsanta' which is highly susceptible to wilt. Where new land is not available, soil sterilization provides the only reliable means of control. Recent research at HRI East Malling has developed a soil ptest to determine levels of verticillium present in soils. This test is now used commercially by growers to assist in disease managment.

For other soft fruit crops, such as cane and bush fruit, IPDM has only

Table 3: Sampling and assessment of pests and diseases

Sampling unit per tree (visual inspection unless beating specified)	Pest/disease
Dormant period 2 vegetative buds in one year shoots 4 branch nodes on 2-3 year old wood Whole tree	apple rust mite fruit tree red spider mite winter eggs wood scab apple mildew (silvered shoots) apple canker and wood rotting fungi
Bud-burst to mouse ear Two outer rosette leaves	apple rust mite
Green cluster to pink bud Whole orchard 4 trusses	rosy leaf curling aphid rosy apple aphid apple grass aphid apple sucker capsid winter or tortrix moth caterpillar primary apple mildew
Whole tree	apple scab
Beat 2 branches	apple blossom weevil
Late blossom to petal fall Whole tree	rosy apple aphid apple scab
4 trusses	apple sawfly winter moth or clouded drab moth capsid fruit tree red spider mite
2 leaves	apple rust mite
Fortnightly after petalfall (June, July, August (and September where necessary)) Whole orchard	collar rot crown rot
Whole tree	rosy apple aphid woolly aphid rosy leaf curling aphid sawfly damage blossom wilt
1-2 year old shoots growing shoots	apple canker green apple aphid clouded drab moth apple scab
5 apical leaves in 2 growing shoots	secondary apple mildew
2 leaves	fruit tree red spider mite apple rust mite
Pheromone traps	codling moth
	fruit tree tortix moth
	summer fruit tortix moth

as the basis for decision making in apple orchards in the UK	
Threshold per 25 trees	**Action if threshold exceeded**
average of 10 mites/bud	Treat at mouse ear/green cluster
>30 nodes with > 5 eggs	Treat with ovicide pre-blossom
presence	Remove during winter pruning
average of 5 mites/outer leaf	Treat as soon as possible pre-blossom
presence	Spot treatment
1 infested	
30 trusses infested	
30 trusses infested	Treat as pink bud
2 trusses infested	
5 trusses infested	
2% mildew blossom	Treat with eradicant fungicide,
	maximise dose, reduce interval
presence	Treat with eradicant/protectant fungicide,
	maximise dose, reduce interval
10 adults	Treat as soon as possible pre-blossom
presence	Treat as petal fall
presence	Treat with eradicant/protectant fungicide,
	maximise dose, reduce interval
10 egg insertions	Treat within 7 days of 80% petal fall
3 caterpillers	Treat at petal fall
2 infested or damaged	
average of 2 mites/leaf	Treat as soon as possible
average of 5 mites/leaf	
presence	Spot treat
presence	Remove tree, treat replant
1-2 colonies	
young extention growth infested	Treat as soon as possible
presence	Spot treatment
presence	Treat following year
presence	Prune out. Treat next year
presence	Prune out. Treat in autumn
4 infested	Treat as soon as possible
3 infested	
presence	Adjust spray interval, rate and product
	choice as necessary
8% mildewed leaves	Treat with eradicant fungicide
	maximise dose, reduce interval
average 2 mites/leaf	
average of 10-50 mites/leaf,	Treat as soon as possible
higher level later in season	
>5 moths/trap/week for 2 weeks	Treat 7-10 days after threshold catch or
not necessarily successive	immediately if using diflubenzuron
>30 moths/trap/week	Treat 7-10 days after threshold catch or
	immediately if using diflubenzuron
>30 moths/trap/week	Treat 7-10 days after threshold catch

recently been considered. In most cases these are not sprayed as intensively as apples, but nevertheless rely on routine treatment for pest and disease control. Pest warning systems have been developed to assist in the timing of sprays for control of cane midge on raspberries. Warning systems, and thresholds for the monitoring of pests and diseases, are still being researched.

And so to conclude, fruit crops are subject to attack by a wide range of pests and diseases which require adequate control measures to achieve the yields of quality fruit demanded by the market. Previously growers have been happy to rely on the use of routine sprays of pesticides, providing the most reliable, least risky and easiest system to manage. However, consumer concerns and difficulties with pesticide resistance have necessitated the adoption of alternative approaches to crop protection.

Integrated pest and disease management provides the best alternative approach, but it requires a much higher grower input with consequent higher costs to achieve the same standards of crop protection achieved previously by chemicals alone. The adoption of IPDM is greatest in apple and pear production where systems are well researched and established and least in soft fruit, where much research is still required.

In apples and pears IPDM has been incorporated into a system of Integrated Fruit Production (IFP) governing all aspects of production from planting to marketing. IFP combines integrated orchard protection with the most advanced horticultural techniques in a system of production that produces high yields of quality fruit with due regard to the environment and human health.

Standards for IFP have been drawn up for the UK and for Europe. While most UK apple and pear producers practise integrated mite management, relatively few are following IFP. However most growers are recognising the value of IFP and are aiming to achieve its production standards in the future.

This work was funded by the Ministry of Agriculture Fisheries and Food.

DR ANGELA BERRIE AND JERRY CROSS *are members of the Crop Protection Department of Horticulture Research International, East Malling. They are both former members of ADAS*

First Aid for Fruit

PIPPA GREENWOOD

WOUNDS OR DECAY on fruit trees may occur as a result of 'natural causes', accidental injury, vandalism – or by design, in the case of pruning. Obviously wherever possible it is best to avoid deliberate wounding, but to maintain the productivity and structure of apples and pears a certain amount of routine pruning is often required. From time to time it may also be necessary to remove diseased or dead wood from large or overgrown fruit trees on occasions.

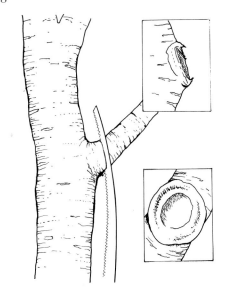

Make a clean cut, leaving the branch collar intact (inset top). The tree is then less susceptable to disease and the wound heals faster (inset, bottom)

It is essential to remove a branch or spur with a clean cut angled so that water and fungal spores cannot readily collect on the cut surface. The cut itself must not be made flush with the main stem or trunk as the branch collar, usually seen as a ridge around the junction between the branch and the trunk, should be left intact. If the branch collar is removed the wound size is not only greater but will callus (heal) over much more slowly. On the other hand, if a long stub or snag is left the area of damaged wood on which spores can land is larger and the development of the callus is also impeded.

Once you have created a wound or discovered a cavity in the trunk or larger limbs of a tree, what should you do? In the past trees were treated rather like injured human beings: wounds and cavities were cleaned and drained and every scrap of injured wood removed, followed by large quantities of wound dressing or paints liberally applied at every opportunity. Large cavities in the centre of trees were even filled with concrete, or bitumen mixed with sand or similar material. These remedies were based on a theory which presumed that once any woody plant had been wounded it had no further defences against fungal infection and so decay could spread unchecked unless all the rotting wood was removed. The current advice, based on research and observation, is as follows. A healthy tree is capable of producing new bark and wood from the edges of a wound. This tissue, the callus, allows wounds to heal over gradually. In general, use of wound paint is now regarded as inadvisable, ineffective and, in some instances, even harmful. However, there are a few exceptions to this rule which I will outline later. Some wound paints have chemical constituents which seem to encourage healing, initially at least, but even these are fairly ineffective in the long term: they do not form a barrier against pathogen entry for long enough to be of much use. Gradually, cracks in the wound paint will develop allowing spores and water to enter. A disease causing organism tends to thrive in this sheltered, humid and warm site and a sealant may therefore protect the infection rather than the tree! In addition, decay may develop and spread hidden from view by the protective paint. One argument states that it is worthwhile applying a wound paint to the edges of a large cut since this may prevent drying out of the callus-forming cells. In general though, I would say that wound paints and sealants are best avoided.

Like every good rule of thumb, there are some exceptions. Wound treatment is usually regarded as essential on fruit trees, particularly plum, cherry, almond, nectarine, peach and other *Prunus* including ornamental types. These are all particularly susceptible to a fungal disease known as silver leaf caused by *Chondrostereum purpureum* which is a 'fresh wound parasite'. This type of pathogen and others such as *Nectria* cankers are only able to enter and cause damage to a freshly created wound, that is one which is less than one month old. In such instances the use of a wound sealant or paint can prevent disease entry and development. To decrease further silver leaf damage it is essential to prune susceptible trees between June and August wherever possible. At this time of year there are fewer spores of the fungus in the air and, in addition, the trees are in a very active stage of growth and so may be able to produce a gum-like substance which seals off an area if it does become contaminated by the fungus. Fungal spread is, therefore, greatly limited. When a wound paint is necessary it should be applied according to the manufacturer's instruction immediately following the creation of the wound. This will greatly reduce the chances of silver leaf or similar infection. One of the most fundamental discoveries in the field of wound treatment is the theory of 'compartmentalisation of decay in trees', work largely attributed to Dr Alex Shigo and his co-workers. This suggests that wounded trees do have further defences which enable them to limit spread of decay.

The wounded or damaged tree can form barriers (walls) or compartments around the injured area and, by this process of compartmentalisation, the spread of decay is much reduced. The tree produces gum-like substances which plug the vessels above and below the wound (wall 1) – the annual rings – so restricting the spread of the infection to the centre of the tree (wall 2) and the medullary rays, thus limiting the spread around the circumference of the tree (wall 3). A fourth wall forms a very important barrier blocking the newly formed annual rings, those formed after wounding has occurred. Together these barriers resist the decay. This means that the most serious damage resulting from a wound is the decay of that wood already present when the injury occurred. This may sound rather a poor effort on behalf of the tree, but it is an effective system – it takes considerable time for existing wood to deteriorate and by the time it has, the tree will have increased in diameter and new supporting, structural wood will have formed.

The compartmentalisation theory means that at Wisley we no longer advise the clearing out of dead wood from a wound or cavity, since by doing this the walls formed around the damaged area are damaged themselves and decay can spread further. In addition it is no longer recommended that water-filled cavities or pockets found in the trunks or larger limbs of trees are cleared out or drained. Although such an area may indeed accumulate water and sap it is now believed that the surface is best left constantly wet. Underneath the layer of water only organisms which are anaerobic (able to live without oxygen) can survive. Most of the decay-causing pathogens are aerobic (they need oxygen to live) and cannot persist in a low oxygen environment of a permanently wet wound. In addition,

the drilling of auger holes and the insertion of pipe to drain the area would obviously breach the barriers formed and so allow further decay to occur. If a hollow is likely to attract birds or squirrels, it is a good idea to block access to the cavity with half an inch (1cm) gauge chicken wire in order to prevent further damage by wildlife!

As I mentioned earlier, the use of concrete and similar materials to fill 'empty spaces' in trees is no longer recommended. This is because the fillers tend to crack or shrink and also provide protection for a pathogen by hiding the extent of the decay from view.

In practice all this means that we should leave well alone and let the tree use its own method of wound healing. In general, interference increases the problem. However, it is important to remember that a tree with any sort of decay or cavity may not be safe. If a tree is large and you are in any doubt as to its safety, even to just one or two of its branches, you should seek the advice of a reputable tree surgeon.

PIPPA GREENWOOD is Senior Plant Pathologist at the RHS Garden Wisley. She is a regular contributor to gardening magazines and BBC's Gardeners' Question Time

Fruit the Natural Way

BOB SHERMAN

THE ARGUMENTS FOR organic husbandry of our land are well-rehearsed and nowadays regularly proclaimed. Although better known now than 10 years ago the principles and practices of organic horticulture are still frequently misunderstood. It is not simply a proposal to abandon all factory-made chemicals and horticultural products; nor is it a replacement of one brand of powders for another; nor is it a neo-Luddite determination to return to the methods of archaic agricultural history. There is, indeed, much sound wisdom passed over the handle of a well-worn spade but techniques and technology have greatly improved the potential for organic gardeners to grow well. In addition more is known about pest and disease life cycles, about soil fertility and about pollution than our grandfathers ever knew.

At the heart of the organic view is a clear intention to cause as little damage to the environment as possible while cultivating the landscape. There is still much research to be done; honest appraisal of new pesticides should not be discarded out of allegiance to historically approved preparations. Nevertheless the message of global pollution cannot be ignored – the intentions of organic gardeners are sound.

So much for the message – what of the practice? After 18 years of growing fruit organically, I would not dare to claim that it is easy! It is, however, possible and fruitful.

Ryton Organic Gardens were created by the Henry Doubleday Research Association (HDRA) and opened in 1986 to provide a visible and tangible showcase for organic methods. The gardens comprise some 30 displays, most featuring fruit and four devoted exclusively to soft or top fruits. So successful has this exercise been that HDRA have been able to develop a second venture at Yalding in Kent and have provided an inspiration to European groups to create their own organic centres.

THE SITE

Five miles south-east of Coventry, the site is decidedly unconducive to fruit growing. Our 8 ha (20 acres) sit in a shallow undulation that is prone to sharp damaging frosts, frequently in late May or early June. In eight years we have recorded at least one frost in every month of the calendar, including August - but, fortunately, not every year! The death of millions of elms has also left Warwickshire an open and sparsely treed county. Demented sub-arctic winds periodically sweep across the landscape, harrying our young plantations and cutting back soft growth, although fences, hedges and young copses go some way to alleviating this. The soil, however, is friendly - a free-draining sandy loam over gravel with a pH of 6.4. Rainfall averages 65 to 70cm (26-28in) per annum. A permanent irrigation system supplies water during the dry months.

THE FRUIT DISPLAYS

For entirely aesthetic reasons the fruit displays are circular in design, the soft fruit being housed in a large fenced, netted and rabbit-proof circular stockade. A double gate allows public access so that visitors can get close to the fruit and even garner a furtive sample. Illicit fruit tastes all the sweeter, thus artfully advancing the organic case.

The soft fruit garden has symmetrically arranged beds of bush-trained red- and whitecurrants, gooseberries, Jostaberries, Worcesterberries, blackcurrants and raspberries and arctic raspberries. Around the perimeter are single, double and triple cordon and fan-trained forms of currants and gooseberries and a selection of blackberries and hybrid berries. At their feet grow strawberries and spring bulbs. Where possible we have chosen cultivars with proven resistance to pest or disease.

Nearby three separate circular displays demonstrate apple, pear and plum growing. The displays attempt to give an immediate, readily visible introduction to as many aspects of top fruit growing as possible: the effect of rootstocks, disease resistant cultivars, pollination requirements, pruning techniques, trained forms including spindle, pyramid, cordon, fan, palmette and espalier. Three cherries complete the top fruit collection. These have been trained as fans along the outside of the Soft Fruit Garden fence.

FERTILITY

Although our soil is readily worked and drains well, it rapidly loses structure and fertility unless it is regularly fed. This is particularly true where soil is left bare for any length of time. Great care is taken at planting time to ensure that soil conditions are right for the fruit. Any poor management at this time cannot easily be remedied later. Subsequent provision for the fruit is based on soil analysis reports and visible signs of deficiency.

Our first soil report from Elm Farm Research Centre (an organic agricultural research centre) indicated possible long term shortages of phosphate but good organic matter levels. With little previous experience to draw from, we tried to translate conventional fertilizer recommendations into an organic fertility plan. We have now revised our views on this, having found that we were supplying too much nitrogen which resulted in excessive growth, wind damage and leaf problems in gooseberries. The long term phosphate levels have been successfully maintained with rock phosphate or basic slag.

Now that we have acquired some hard-earned experience of our own, we are able to suggest the following pre-planting preparations:

1. If the land is under grass, turn in the turf rather than remove it. Much fertility and humus are lost by stripping and removing the surface cover.

2. If the land is not under grass, apply garden compost at the rate of one 50kg

(110lb) wheelbarrow to every 2 to 3 sq m (2½-32 sq ft). If no compost is available use a low nutrient soil improver such as wood fibre, leafmould, hop waste or coir.

3. Farmyard manure should not be applied excessively. The recommended rate is one barrowful to every 10 sq m (108 sq ft). This may look parsimonious but is perfectly adequate. Redcurrants, gooseberries and blackberries will not need manure unless the soil is particularly poor. Garden compost can be substituted for these.

4. It surprises many to discover that we rarely use organic fertilizers. We have used them, however, in advance of planting fruits. Hoof and horn, a source of nitrogen, seaweed meal for trace elements and potash and bonemeal supplying phosphate are worked into the top 15 cm (6 in) of soil at rates based on advice given by Elm Farm. These rates will vary from garden to garden.

From the middle of May bushes and trees are mulched with a thick layer of damp hay. We had thought that we would need to provide additional fertilizer in the form of compost or manure every year but we have found this unnecessary. Although the hay is removed in late winter it appears to be providing a steady supply of nutrients. In eight years we have applied garden compost to our soft fruit only once, used a concentrated pelleted manure on our raspberries for the first time in spring 1994 and applied seaweed meal only once in 1987 to the gooseberries to try to provide some potash as a balance to the excessive nitrogen. Periodically soil samples are taken for analysis but so far these have not indicated any major deficiencies in the soil.

WEED CONTROL

There are no permitted herbicides under European organic standards. This means that weed control must be manual. Since most amateur gardeners do not use weedkillers around fruit, our displays are immediately appropriate to our visitors' own experience.

In the immediate post-planting period there is a danger of perennial weeds from the incorporated turf becoming irreversibly well-established. To prevent any chance of this, all bushes and trees are given a mulch of overlapping cardboard covered in damp hay. From then on only the hay covering has to be renewed and the occasional determined dandelion hand pulled. In a wet season the hay can begin to grow a green haze of young grass. The remedy is to turn it upside down.

Strawberries are not mulched until fruits begin to form. Annual weeds frequently appear in the rows during this time except where the crop is growing through a soil cover such as Mypex or Phormisol (woven polypropylene fabric). Regular hoeing in spring is usually sufficient, and any survivors can easily be removed by hand.

PESTS AND DISEASES

Organic husbandry is not a panacea for pest-free crops nor is it necessarily an open invitation to all-comers to have unopposed access to leaves and fruit. The sprayer does form part of the strategy but not as the first option. There is still use of the traditional remedies such as Bordeaux mixture for bacterial canker of plums and cherries. Improved technology and techniques give us pheromone traps, greater understanding of pest/predator relationships, better knowledge of pest and disease life cycles, more effective pruning and, not least, much improved cultivars.

Attracting beneficial insects is an important priority in organic growing. Wherever possible appropriate flowers are grown close to fruit to attract anthocorids, hoverflies and lacewings. One of the simplest ways of achieving this is to grow wildflower strips as close to the crop as possible. At the experimental orchard at Lincoln College in New Zealand, Bob Crowder has shown how allowing a dense flower-rich meadow to grow in the alleys right up to the canopy of the apple trees has greatly improved pest control without spraying. Such plantings are very easy to manage when established, requiring cutting just once a year, although they could provide competition for water and nutrients.

Resistant cultivars offer an increasing choice for gardeners. The introduction of the red-fruited gooseberry 'Martlet' in 1995 will increase to four the cultivars free of American gooseberry mildew. In blackcurrants and raspberries progress has been equally encouraging. There is a selection of scab-free apple cultivars and our emphasis on this criterion led us to overlook powdery mildew, which has now shown itself to be more of a problem.

Pheromone traps are, I believe, still in their infancy. We use codling and plum fruit moth traps which although not eliminating the problem, reduce damage to acceptable levels. We are not, after all, aiming at a supermarket Class 1 grade-out for every fruit.

Cultural techniques have always featured strongly in the gardener's methods and we still make good use of finger and thumb, secateurs and saw. Remov-

ing early signs of diseases, such as powdery mildew, and keen eyed regular inspections to follow have proved perfectly adequate. The single pin-holed gooseberry leaf deep in the canopy may contain the only sawfly colony in that bush. One leaf is easy to remove; twenty fat grubs are not!

The organic arsenal of sprays is not extensive. European organic standards allow only sulphur and Bordeaux mixture for fungal problems and derris, pyrethrum and insecticidal soap for pests. Biological controls, such as *Bacillus thuringiensis* for lepidopteran larvae or *Phytoseiulus persimilis* for spider mite, are allowed but we have not had cause to use them.

There is currently no easy way to introduce new products to the accepted list. This problem needs to be addressed since many new developments in pest control products may well prove more acceptable environmentally than those currently approved for, I suspect, essentially historical reasons.

Fruit can be found in almost all of the 30 demonstration gardens at Ryton. They are used educationally, ornamentally, inspirationally and – weather permitting on our inhospitable site – even edibly. Books on organic growing are now plentiful, but we aim to put real pictures on to a living page with growing examples of organic fruit. We invite you to come and see for yourself.

For information contact Ryton Gardens, Ryton-on-Dunsmore, Coventry CV3 3LG. Tel: 01203 303517

BOB SHERMAN is Gardens Curator to the Henry Doubleday Research Association and a member of the RHS Fruit Group Committee

The Development of Pest and Disease Resistance in Apples at HRI

Frank Alston

Genetic resistances have been found to most diseases and pests of apple, but it is not practicable to introduce them all into a breeding programme and give sufficient attention to the main aim: the production of high-yielding cultivars with high fruit quality and good storage and shelf life.

The priorities for breeding disease and pest-resistant cultivars are based on economics and depend on the cost of the breeding programme and the degree to which costs will be reduced and market value increased by the production of resistant cultivars. The main concerns are therefore those diseases and pests which would have a direct effect on fruit quality and which need to be controlled by expensive spray programmes. There are good prospects for producing new top-quality apple cultivars which can be grown and stored to a high standard in integrated production systems with much reduced spray regimes.

The two diseases in apples which account for most of the outlay in fungicides, scab (*Venturia inaequalis*) and mildew (*Podosphaera leucotricha*), have received the most attention. However, concern over chemical residues in food has resulted in a change of emphasis by HRI (Horticulture Research International). The development of new cultivars which can be stored and marketed successfully without the aid of late-season sprays or post-harvest dips is more important.

Most apple pests can be controlled by predators or other practices of integrated control. However, rosy apple aphid *(Dysaphis plantaginea)* cannot be controlled adequately by these methods, so resistance to this pest is an important breeding objective.

STORAGE POTENTIAL

There are good prospects of new cultivars which will store well without pre- or post-harvest sprays. After screening a wide range of apples for storage potential, the new HRI cultivars 'Fiesta' and 'Falstaff' were found to be among the most promising, combining high fruit quality, high yield and some ability to store well without post-harvest dips.

Consequently, these two cultivars, each with such a valuable attribute, are important parents in the current HRI breeding programme. Recently, 10 selections from crosses involving 'Fiesta' were passed to orchard trials following selection for good storage performance and quality assessment on the basis of fruit firmness, acidity and sugar content.

SCAB (*VENTURIA INAEQUALIS*) RESISTANCE

Widespread pathogenic variation is known in *V. inaequalis*. Of the five genes identified as providing universal resistance to the disease organism, that derived from *Malus floribunda* has been most widely used by breeders. None of the recently released scab-resistant cultivars shows all the characteristics associated with high quality fruit in Northern Europe. Two HRI selections combining scab resistance with a distinct 'Cox'-type flavour have performed well at unsprayed sites in Switzerland, but both yield poorly and form trees unsuitable for intensive growing systems. Further crossing in 1987 using 'Fiesta', 'Gala' and 'Falstaff' as commercial parents has resulted in promising high-yielding, 'Cox'-type, good storing, scab-resistant selections for trial and more are expected in the near future. Heavy regular cropping, good texture and appearance and scab resistance are combined in another HRI selection. This is a well coloured selection which also resists mildew well and has shown better fruit quality than the widely planted, scab-resistant French cultivar, 'Florina' in trials in France and Switzerland. It has not the highly aromatic, acidic 'Cox'-type flavour, but is sweet with a crisp, juicy texture.

The recent identification, at two sites, of *V. inaequalis* strains which are virulent on scab-resistant derivatives of *M. floribunda* raises doubt about the durability of that type of resistance. However, the situation is complicated, since it appears that not all scab-resistant *M. floribunda* derivatives are susceptible to the two strains.

Besides attempts to achieve durable resistance to scab by combining resistance genes in breeding programmes, new sources of resistance are being investigated at HRI.

MILDEW (*PODOSPHAERA LEUCOTRICHA*) RESISTANCE

Some cultivars such as 'Jonagold' and 'Golden Delicious' carry a high level of mildew resistance when compared to very susceptible cultivars such as 'Cox's Orange Pippin', 'Jonathan' and 'Idared'. Although this type of resistance rarely provides full protection, it is sufficient in some areas to allow economic cropping without sprays. Mildew resistance of this type is combined with scab resistance from *M. floribunda* in HRI apple selections.

In regions with a high natural incidence of the disease, full control can only be attained by very intensive spray programmes, up to 17 applications each growing season in south-eastern England. To give the same effect, high levels of resistance have been transferred from the ornamental species *M. zumi* and *M. robusta* at HRI. Good fruit size and quality, combined with strong mildew resistance from these species, was achieved by the second backcross to commercial apples. Recently, resistant cultivars with high yield potential and improved fruit quality have been chosen for orchard trials from a third backcross. A number of third backcross progenies combined mildew resistance with scab resistance from *M. floribunda*. Promising high quality selections, which combine high levels of mildew and scab resistance, have been selected from these HRI progenies.

ROSY APPLE APHID (*DYSAPHIS PLANTAGINEA*) RESISTANCE

A high level of resistance to this aphid is carried by the *M. robusta* donor of mildew resistance. At HRI it has proved to be convenient to transfer aphid resistance concurrently with mildew resistance. In common with scab and mildew, greenhouse selection of young resistant seedlings is possible. Resistant seedlings can be identified by a hyper-sensitive reaction only five days after inoculation. An outstanding resistant 'Cox'-type selection from the second backcross of *M. robusta* to commercial apples is currently being used in the HRI breeding programme. Selections carrying resistance to mildew, scab and rosy apple aphid have been made from crosses between this selection and another which is scab resistant. These are awaiting selection for yield and fruit quality.

DEVELOPING NEW APPLE CULTIVARS AT HRI

High fruit quality and high productivity remain the main aims of the HRI apple breeding programme. Market and consumer requirements, in particular the current search for new and distinct products, have a special influence on the apple breeding policy of HRI. Flavour, texture, appearance, storage period and shelf life are all given prior-ity over disease resistance. While there is room for compromise over relative levels of resistance to various diseases and pests, there is very little scope for compromise over quality components in this programme. For example, in one progeny, after stringent selection for the optimum level of fruit acidity, only 11 per cent of seedlings remained. Further to this, a consideration of seven principal characteristics, yield, skin finish, fruit colour, fruit size, acidity, storage and texture, but excluding disease and pest resistance in several progenies, showed that in respect of the best, only 1 per cent of seedlings could be expected to be suitable for orchard trials. Selections for disease and pest resistance is moderated to allow stringent selection to achieve the necessarily high quality standards required by the consumer. Disease and pest resistance will be introduced progressively, and combined with yield and quality features as components become available. The new HRI cultivar 'Fiesta' marks the start of such a development, carrying some ability to store without post-harvest dips along with high yield and quality.

Strategic research directed towards the incorporation of disease and pest resistance and the improvement of quality is supported by the Ministry of Agriculture, Fisheries and Food. This includes searching for genetic markers to aid efficient early slection. The development of new cultivars is supported by the East Malling Apple and Pear Breeding Club, an industry-based group including the Apple and Pear Research Council, Pépinières du Valois and the New Zealand Apple and Pear Marketing Board. HRI also co-ordinates the EEC-supported project for the development of the European Apple Crop. This project, involving eight nations, is to develop advanced breeding methods, principally genome mapping, to aid the efficient integration of disease resistance and improved quality into the European apple.

Finally, HRI has a collaborative arrangement involving breeding apples for disease resistance with the Swiss

Federal Resarch Station, Wädenswil.

This article is based on a paper presented at Workshop on the development of scab and mildew resistant apple varieties at Arhrweiler, Germany, December 1993

D R F R A N K A L S T O N *is in charge of tree fruit breeding at Horticulture Research International, East Malling*

Cuckoo in June

DAVID ATKINS

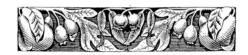

I STARTED GROWING apples in 1954. There were a number of eccentrics about in those days; they had come back from the war and with land at £100 an acre had opted for the simple life and started up orchards.

One was Brian Marston whose passion was for old machinery which he could not resist buying. When spraying young apple trees he drove a thundering tractor which towed a large trailer on which was a tank and a thumping diesel pump. Behind the lot trailed a long thin pipe, and at the far end – a small New Zealand girl with a lance. A knapsack would have done the same job. As a result of his farming methods he was often besieged by creditors, so he lived up a steep hill in a wooden hut built originally for his father's mistress.

Few creditors could make the climb.

My next door neighbour would only employ girls. He drank hugely, dealt only in cash, and his wife paid out £5 (worth £100 today) to anyone who brought him home at night. He was delivered back legless two or three times a week.

With such colourful competition I quickly found myself doing reasonably well. Nowadays my competitors are eager young men with national diplomas in horticulture. They take air temperatures both by day and night, take moisture readings of the soil at different levels and put all the results and many more on to computers. They produce apples which do not have the flavour and delight of the old 'Cox's Orange Pippin'. They are not to blame for this, it is the great supermarkets who wish us to grow large apples all of the same colour and size.

A few things have become better, and one of these is spraying. In the 1950s the only spray we had for codling moth was lead arsenate. We put this on twice a year, normally on about 15 June and then for the second generation, three weeks later. It was a spray dangerous to men and insects and we apple growers pressed the research stations to find something safer. The problem with spraying is to find something that kills the bug you are after, but yet does not kill the other insects. Lead arsenate killed everything. As a result it was often followed by devastating attacks of red spider because, while it had killed the live spiders, it did not kill their eggs. These then hatched and there was nothing left alive to eat them. Friendly insects are the ladybird, the black kneed capsid, the lacewing and others.

The gradual 'greening' of apple growing began long, long before the general public ever thought of it. We used, four days after blossom fall, to put on 20 ounces per acre of a chemical to kill sawfly. This spray, however, also killed any bees which were unwise enough to visit the fruit tree after the blossom had gone. (Bees can still get honey out of petal-less blooms for a few days.) We gradually reduced this to 10 ounces, then to five ounces, to two ounces and now it is very rarely used because of the danger to bees and beneficial insects.

There used to be an attitude of bravado among experienced fruit men. They considered wearing protective clothing and helmets as rather wimpish. Long before it was legally necessary we brought protective clothing into regular use. Certainly in 35 years of growing we have never had anyone, except possibly myself, even slightly affected by spray and I do not know of anyone in England who has been incapacitated by fruit spraying. This is rather extraordinary when one thinks that early on we put on dangerous winter washes by hand lance, which, if splashed onto the skin, turned it a dirty yellow .

Many years later, as soon as he came into the business, my son insisted that we cut our spray rates by two thirds and that we bought a cab tractor with a charcoal filter which purifies the air breathed by the driver. This has been a great pleasure for everyone. Men are able to spray all day without wearing oilskins and without getting dirty. The irritating thing is that by law one still has to wear oilskins for mixing up the spray materials even though we use only those of low toxicity.

Spraying has various objectives. The simplest is spraying for insect damage. We have now been able to cut that down to one spray for both caterpillars and aphids and two sprays for codling. In the old days aphids were very difficult to kill and one could only get them in the two days after they had hatched and before the bud opened. For caterpillars we spray when the base leaves on the buds are the size of a fingernail. The second objective is to give nutrients to the leaves. For that purpose we spray three times a year with Epsom salt to give them magnesium and also frequently with small doses of urea for nitrogen, seaweed extract for trace elements and calcium which is needed by growing apples. Guano would be excellent, but it is not available.

The third objective is to stop scab and powdery mildew spreading. That is the difficult one and we spray three or four times early on to protect the emerging young leaves against the attack of fungal spores. If the spores fail to get an early foothold on the leaves one can stop spraying early. We would like to grow organically and stop using chemicals, but I notice that apple trees in private gardens, while they get into balance with insects, are normally a mass of scab, mildew and canker. Organic apples at the moment are, in my opinion, impossible to grow properly, but it may come.

Bees are a lazy lot of layabouts. If the weather is cold they don't get up in the morning. When one has hired in 40 hives at £10 each and placed them strategically throughout the orchards it is quite maddening to see that by half past ten on a cold morning not one bee has emerged to work. However, the bumble bee with its furry coat is impervious to cold and gets out and about in all weathers. These brave insects nest in the ground and under hedges; over the years I have become very fond of them and will always help them out from behind window panes and feed them honey if they are exhausted. They can now be bought, 30 bees to a hive, but they are expensive.

Another maddening habit of bees is that they tend to get hooked on the wrong crop. Bluebells come out just before apple blossom and bees love them, as they do that yellow invader of the countryside, oilseed rape. Bees home in on rape, but from it they make poor honey with a bad flavour; their honey solidifies quickly in the hives and is difficult to harvest. To stop the bees getting and staying on the wrong crop one can move them a minimum of five miles, as the crow flies, from their home base. If you then put them down in the middle of an orchard which is already flowering they may condescend to help with the apple blossom. If you put them there a day too early and before the apple blossom is producing nectar, they will be off to the nearest bluebell wood or rape field and return there each trip.

Even if they are put in the middle of an orchard with the blossom out and full of nectar they are quite capable of going for the dandelions in the grass. Dandelions lie so flat to the ground that they are very difficult to cut with a mower, but as a routine one should cut the grass before the bees come in. When placing hives put them in the sun and nowhere near another grower's orchard. You, not he, have paid for them and they are there to work for you. Hives are placed at night. It is a tricky job because, when moving them, their entrances have to be closed off with enough grass to let in sufficient air for the bees to breathe but which doesn't fall out when the bee hives are bumping along on a trailer. Also, as the hive is made of loosely joined segments ensure it is tied firmly with rope as it may come apart. Fortunately bees cannot see in the dark and if a hive disintegrates one just has to switch off the lights and move away. If attacked in daylight and near trees, run through them but never in a straight line. Astonishingly bees are bad at turning corners.

Picking appeals to the squirrelling instinct of human beings and there are very few people who do not enjoy harvesting. It is an ancient race memory and, even if they don't recognise it at first, everybody has it. They find themselves caught up by the feeling that they are doing something natural which will help feed their group through the winter to come and to our amazement and gratitude will turn up to work in the most dreadful weather. Good pickers are invaluable.

For the English apple grower the narrow dates within which the crop has to be 'got' presents a major problem. Harvest is easy for the South Africans, the New Zealanders and the Americans who all have several main cultivars which crop over a long period. The 'Cox', which is so temperamental, is our main apple. It crops in England at a maximum of 10 tons an acre while all other commercial varieties throughout the world crop regularly at between 20 and 30 tons an acre.

My son, who spent six months working on a fruit farm in South Africa, remarked that because of their warm summer and extended season, they had no problems with getting the trees to crop and so their pruning was very simple. Their growing does not have to be so precise but the quality of their packing and marketing is very good. With their high production and long season they sell on the English market, receive the proceeds in pounds and pay their expenses in cheap rand. They therefore make very heavy profits per acre, indeed fantastic profits of some 10 times as much as the best growers in England can achieve.

You may have heard my book *The Cuckoo in June* when it was serialized on BBC Radio 4. I called it that as apple growers are vanishing fast, and like June cuckoos may soon all be gone. One of the causes have been a Civil Service dedicated to free trade, and as the House of Commons Select Committee said: 'Other EC countries are more generous, more ingenious and more devious in assisting their growers'. Also, growing is very labour intensive, and for the cost of one man in England, one can employ 14 in South Africa and South America and 10 in Poland. My staff did not take kindly to my suggestion of a rate of 50 pence an hour!

Finally supermarkets are far more dominant in England than in any other country. Couple this with a public, who unlike the French and the Germans, give little support to their own country's produce, and the supermarkets buy the cheapest which is mainly from abroad; as a result all English vegetable and fruit growers are being wiped out. We were 4,000 when I started and we are now down to 400.

DAVID ATKINS is a fruit grower in Pulborough, West Sussex. This article is adapted from his book The Cuckoo in June *in its 5th reprint.*

Our European counterparts

HOWARD STRINGER

WE IN THE United Kingdom are very fortunate. We have a comprehensive collection of fruit cultivars in the National Fruit Collection at Brogdale, in Kent, together with a smaller collection of the more garden-worthy cultivars at Wisley. This is thanks to the combined efforts of the Royal Horticultural Society and the Ministry of Agriculture in the 1920s in gathering a collection of fruits for trial at Wisley and the Herculean labours of food and wine writer Morton Shand during the war years. He publicised the importance of preserving our fruit heritage, exhorting the public to look out for old unknown fruit trees and to send in specimens for identification. Perhaps we tend to take Brogdale for granted, for it was once thought that as it was owned by the State it was in safe hands, but recent events have made this less certain.

On the Continent, however, although there are many collections belonging to universities and schools of horticulture, there is nothing like the magnificent collection at Brogdale. The marketing revolution of the 1970s, which resulted in orchards of a multiplicity of old and tried local cultivars being grubbed up and replaced by relatively few standardised kinds such as 'Golden Delicious' and 'Jonagold',

appears to have been the common spur for European enthusiasts to try to preserve their heritage, while the old cultivars were still around to be rescued. First it was necessary to contact other like-minded people, then to form organisations. Land had to be bought to plant trees, and the establishment of orchards meant finding volunteer helpers willing to maintain them. All things which are an accomplished fact of life in the United Kingdom.

The need for contact between members led to the foundation of newsletters, in most cases quarterly, and all vibrant with interest. With this history, it is perhaps understandable that the difference between European amateur fruit growers and ourselves is the high priority given on the Continent to preserving the old cultivars and the emphasis on growing them in the traditional way - that is, as standard trees.

In France there is the 'Croquers de Pommes', or 'Apple Crunchers'. They were founded in 1978 by Jean Choisel and to cover such a large country with a great variation in climate, they have evolved into 19 regional groups. The process has been speeded up by associating with established pomological groups such as the Société Pomologique du Berry. They have a particularly large task, for it has been estimated that there are at least 4,000 local apple cultivars in France alone, almost twice the number of apples at Brogdale! The name 'Apple Crunchers' was deliberately chosen to be humorous, but it does not mean that their interest is solely confined to that fruit. The organisation now has several conservation orchards in various parts of the country, holding collections ranging from apples and pears to figs, nuts and olives. Membership has grown from a handful in 1978 to over 2,000 in 1993, distributed over the whole country. A quarterly newsletter, *Le Bulletin*, is published, to keep members in touch.

Belgium is the home of the Nationale Boomgaarden Stichting, or National Orchard Foundation. This is the culmination of efforts by its founder Ludo Royen to preserve Belgium's regional cultivars. He started by forming a collection of 500 cultivars from his own region. Giving the occasional lecture, he slowly gathered round him a group of like-minded people and after a successful exhibition at the University of Limburg in 1984, decided to give his group a formal shape and the Foundation was born. Its headquarters is the University of Limburg, Diepenbeek, at the centre of a fertile fruit-growing area, and there are regional branches at Mechelen (Malines) and the western part of the province of Brabant, which includes Brussels. The first edition of their newsletter, *Pomologia,* appeared in 1985, in the Flemish language. A French language edition was launched some years later, but unfortunately was not read by enough people to justify the cost of production.

This Trust works closely with other European countries and besides their own fruit show held every autumn, co-operates in staging a pan-European show, called Europom, every four years which is held, where possible, in different countries. In October 1993 this took place at a castle in Limburg province in Belgium, where with the participation of five other countires, including the United Kingdom, over 1,500 fruit cultivars were staged. The Trust has about 1,100 members and is remarkable for its range and the number of its meetings, about 30 per year, which include visits to orchards, theoretical lectures and practical demonstrations. They have established about 15 orchards in various parts of Belgium to house their collections and where they can hold demonstrations. A great bonus to members is the annual sale of fruit trees. In 1992, 175 cultivars of apple were offered; 100 of pear, 67 of cherry, 72 of plum and 15 of peach, together with many cultivars of soft fruit. They have also developed a computer programme to speed up the identification of the masses of fruit that is always brought along at shows.

Holland is the home of the Noordelijke Pomologische Vereniging, or Northern Pomological Association. This was formed in 1989 and is centred around the town of Assen in Drenthe province. Some meetings take place in the neighbouring province of Groningen. They had about 350 members in 1993. They hold a show every other year in autumn in a school of horticulture specialising in fruit in the small town of Frederiksoord near Assen, and the next one will be in 1996.

This Association is also working on the computerised determination of apples. Its greatest wish has been to have a place where it could house its collection of about 750 apple cultivars, 130 pears and 130 plums, which were dispersed in members' gardens, and it has recently been offered about 2 ha (5 acres) of land in Frederiksoord with which to make a start, with the promise that further land will be made available at a later date. The Association has a policy of reprinting facsimile versions of old pomological works in order to bring them within the reach of their members. Perhaps its greatest triumph in this area has been the reissue of *Pomologia* and *Fructologia* (1750) by the great Dutch pomologist Knoop.

Germany has been the last country to revive an organisation to preserve its heritage of fruit. In the later years of the last century there had existed a Society of German Pomologists, a rather highbrow association of learned professionals, which was dissolved after the First World War. A male nurse named Gert Müller, a passionate amateur fruit lover who already had gathered a collection of 350 apples, conceived the idea in the 1980s of launching a modern successor to that organisation. He realised that all over Germany there were enthusiasts like himself who were doing their own little bit to keep local cultivars of fruit alive, but needed the encouragement of fellowship to stimulate interest. He gathered a number of enthusiasts together for a meeting in the village of Barnstorf, south-west of Bremen, in October 1990 to propose the founding of a formal organisation.

At that meeting the Association of Pomologists was born. The founders were quick to point out that the word 'German' had been deliberately dropped from the title because they intended their organisation to have links with neighbouring countries, for after all, fruits of German origin did not stop growing at the frontier. Also, they stressed that 'Pomologist' should be taken to mean any lover of fruit.

Since then, the Association has been successfully divided into regions and an annual yearbook is published. By early 1992 it had attracted about 80 members and aims to collect 1,200 cultivars of apple, to be planted in two areas, a 7 ha (18 acre) plot of rented land near Barnstorf and in the grounds of a school of horticulture at Triesdorf near Nuremberg. It is interesting to read of the difficulty this organisation has had in renting land. There was plenty available, but the owner would ask for what purpose the land was wanted and when told that it was for planting fruit trees, would refuse to let it. Apparently the local farmers could not conceive that land could be used for any other purpose than for an annual crop!

The Association's AGM takes place towards the close of a weekend meeting of fellowship, discussions and book and plant exchanges held in a local inn in a different part of Germany every year.

Switzerland is home to the organisation Fructus, founded in 1985, and they held their first show in 1986. By 1994 they had over 700 members. At a magnificent show in 1992, in conjunction with Pro Specie Rara, an organisation devoted to the preservation of threatened wildlife species, animals as well as plants, they exhibited 650 cultivars of apple. A quarterly newsletter is published, in separate German and French language editions, and a limited number of copies is available for purchase by members of the public.

Thus progress has been swift in all

cases to provide the necessary infrastructure to ensure that local varieties of fruit are kept alive and in the consciousness of the consumer, thanks to the hard work and dedication of many enthusiasts. May we wish them every success!

Summary of Organisations
France: Association Nationale des Croquer de Pommes. President: Claude Scribe. Address: Sente des Brosses, F-77580 VOUCANGIS.

Belgium: Nationale Boomgaaren Stichting. Correspondence address: Postbus 49, B-3500 HASSELT.

Holland: Noordelijke Pomologische Vereniging. Correspondence address: Sluisstraat 165, NL-9406 AX ASSEN.

Germany: Pomologen-Verein e.V. Chairman: Gert Müller. Address: Meierkamp 1, D-49406 EYDELSTADT-GOTHEL.

Switzerland: Fructus. Address: President, Dr K Stoll, Waisenhausstrasse 4, CH-8820 WADENSWIL.

HOWARD STRINGER, fruit enthusiast, is a member of the RHS Fruit Group Committee and the Brogdale Horticultural Trust Friends Working Party

France

Belgium

Holland

Switzerland

Obstbäume
sind
Lebensräume

Germany

Reflections on Fruit

Bob Sanders

IN THE YEARS before the Second World War my family lived in a cottage in the grounds of an estate in Kent where my father was employed. Behind the cottage was the kitchen garden laid out in the Victorian manner with rolled gravel paths and neatly clipped box hedging surrounding each bed. It was bounded on one side by a high brick wall on which were trained fruit trees of all kinds. On the other side was an old orchard which was underplanted with currants and gooseberry bushes. There were various buildings including a vinery, peach house and several pit-type greenhouses. It was at this home that my childhood memories were formed particularly in relation to fruit growing.

Among the fruits that come to mind from this period was a small plum tree which bore a heavy crop of small round golden fruits with red spots each year. They were delicious eaten from the tree and my mother made an excellent apricot-tasting jam. With hindsight this tree was probably a 'Mirabelle', beloved in France but hardly known in this country. In the orchard there was a tall rather gaunt apple tree. We knew it as the 'Hunting Apple'. It produced small crops of round, flat apples rather like 'Devonshire Quarrenden'. The skin was an even dark red which took a wonderful shine when polished. The flesh was white and stained red in places. We thought it delicious and my sister and I searched the long grass at the foot of the tree every autumn for a good windfall. Could this have been 'Gascoyne's Scarlet' an old Kent apple raised at Sittingbourne?

I attended the village school, and one day a new teacher arrived who had apparently been a missionary in China. As well as the curious artefacts she showed us, we were introduced to silkworms – lots of them. I became the chief supplier of the silkworms' staple food, mulberry leaves. There was an old mulberry tree in the grounds of the hall, which like many of its kind, had gone over and grew at an angle of 45 degrees. It was a black mulberry, *Morus nigra*, and my mother used to gather the fruit by laying a sheet beneath the tree while I ran up the sloping trunk and rocked it to shake the fruit off. We loved its sweet sharp flavour. Now most authorities state that silkworms only eat the leaves of the white mulberry, *Morus alba*, whose fruits are insignificant, but I can assure you that our worms thrived on the leaves from our tree and eventually formed their golden orange cocoons.

Then came the war and my father's job disappeared overnight. In November 1940, we moved and eventually settled in an isolated hamlet between

Newton Abbot and Totnes in South Devon. With hindsight, despite missing our cottage and the lovely garden, the move was providential. We had been very close to Biggin Hill fighter station which had been under regular enemy attack during and after the Battle of Britain. Inevitably bombs had fallen off target and caused damage in our village. In 1944 our cottage was demolished by a doodlebug and subsequently the garden and grounds as I knew them have long ceased to exist.

There was only a small garden at our new home at Stoney Hill – an apt name as the soil was shallow and stony. However, we had strawberries, blackcurrants, and some wonderful raspberries. The raspberry was 'The Devon', one of George Pyne's introductions and despite the shallow soil the canes were very vigorous reaching 2.4m (8ft) in height and cropping well. They did very well for about 10 years – perhaps because we lived in relative isolation one and a half miles from the nearest main road – but eventually the canes lost vigour and cropping tailed off. I doubt very much whether any virus-free stocks of that cultivar exist today, but it certainly served us well. For winter fruit we had apples. My father would go to an orchard in the village, select a well laden tree and agree a price for the crop with the farmer. We then picked the fruit and struggled home with it in bushel boxes balanced on the carriers of our bicycles. We usually had 'Newton Wonder' as it cooks and keeps well and in the New Year it also makes an acceptable dessert apple. At the time I mistakenly thought 'Newton Wonder' was a local apple, the Newton part of its name relating to Newton Abbot and not to its

true home Kings Newton in Derbyshire.

Time passed and I joined the regular army. Nobody would automatically associate fruit as part of a soldier's diet save perhaps for the inevitable and unchanging plum and apple jam fed to our troops in the First World War. However, in September 1950 I found myself with my regiment, the Argyll and Sutherland Highlanders, together with the Middlesex Regiment, in Korea as part of a United Nation's force holding back the invaders from the communist North. I had read a little about Korea but no mention of the excellent apples grown there. Korea had been under Japanese suzerainty for many years and at that time was very much a peasant society. The Japanese had studied apple growing in the United States and thus most of the apples planted in Korean orchards were of the 'McIntosh' and 'Jonathan' type. These were not perhaps what we would have selected from choice but as hungry soldiers we enjoyed them. The Korean winter is very severe and there the fruit was stored in pits or clamps much as is done with potatoes. A large diameter pit 90cm (3ft) deep was dug and thickly lined with rice straw. The apples were put in and covered with more straw. Finally the displaced soil was shovelled over the pit to form a domed cover. The pit would be opened up when fruit was needed.

I have always enjoyed apples and as a non smoker I usually had plenty of issue cigarettes with which to barter. The South Koreans, whom we were supposed to be defending, would drive a hard bargain for their fruit or eggs. When we advanced into North Korea, 'enemy territory', it was therefore surprising that they apparently welcomed us with open arms by the civilian population. There were triumphal arches of pine branches with the greeting 'Welcome UN Forces' at the entrance to towns and villages. Where south of the 38th Parallel 20 Camel cigarettes might secure three or four apples, whole sackfuls of apples would be hoisted cheerily into the back of our trucks with no question of payment. I have always wondered did they genuinely welcome us as liberators from the communist regime or did they hope by their generosity to deflect the worse effects of the 'brutal and licentious soildiery'?

We returned to our stations in Hong Kong in May 1951, and after local leave resumed the routine of army life: evenings drinking local San Miguel beer, avoiding mosquitoes and trying not the breathe-in too deeply the malodorous airs that came off the surrounding paddy fields. We renewed our acquaintance with that most Chinese of fruits, the lychee. I don't recall seeing it growing in Hong Kong but it turned up in the cookhouse at regular intervals with the evening meal. At one end there would be a large heap of lychees still attached to their branches. One selected a suitable batch and took them to a table to pick and eat them. While this may seem quaint it must be realised that there was room for only one company at a time to eat their meal. Six companies had to be fed and it was the practice to take turns to eat first each day. If one was unfortunate enough to be the last company on a lychee day the scene on arrival was very unappetising with lychee stones and sticks everywhere. Not surprisingly lychees are not my favourite fruits.

In 1954, having married, I decided

that soldiering was not wholly compatible with a normal home life and so I left the army and joined the Kent Police. We started our married life in a furnished flat in the Medway towns with a grape vine and a pear tree in the garden. We learned that unripe grapes make an excellent gooseberry-type jam, and that pickled pears are a first class accompaniment to cold meats. In the years that followed, which included seven house moves, we grew soft fruit in all but one of the gardens. Unfortunately, as there was always the possibility of a move at short notice from one police house to another no one was ever prepared to plant fruit trees. However, in 1971, constabulary housing policy having changed, for the first time we became the proud owners of a house and garden that was ours to plant however we wished.

Our new garden contained six half-standard trees which were probably planted when the house was built in the mid 1930s. There were three apples and three pears and we eagerly awaited the arrival of our first crop. This was a disappointment as the apples were all early dessert and would not keep beyond mid-September. Of the pears, one, a small stunted tree, turned out to be 'Williams' Bon Chrétien', the second never did produce any fruit, and the third, probably 'Laxton's Superb', obviously had fireblight. Having discovered the fireblight, I contacted the Ministry of Agriculture office at Wye to report it. With my constabulary tuned mind I naively expected their arrival within the hour, our garden to be declared an 'Infected Area', the removal of the affected tree and its destruction carried out with clinical efficiency! I was sadly disappointed when they merely suggested that 'It would be best to get rid of it'! All the trees were eventually grubbed and vegetables grown for a year or so.

I next entered what I term my 'gooseberry phase'. On visiting Canterbury one day I purchased a copy of the *Good Fruit Guide* (1984) by Lawrence Hills of Henry Doubleday fame and I was hooked. I could not believe that so many gooseberry cultivars were known, when only 'Careless', 'Leveller', and perhaps 'Whinham's Industry' were found in most garden centres. I read everything I could find on the subject and in the library of Wye College discovered *The Fruit Manual* (1860) by Hogg and Lindley's *A Guide to the Orchard* and *Kitchen Garden* (1831). Gooseberry bushes and cuttings were obtained from various sources, which included the then National Fruit Trials at Brogdale, Manchester University's Trial Grounds at Jodrell Bank, and the Nordic Gene Bank which holds many old British cultivars no longer in our collections. I began a correspondence with Dave Smith of Bolton, a very knowledgeable gooseberry enthusiast, who proved a great source of information. I had a very enjoyable time, eventually growing 75 cultivars and learning a great deal.

I soon realised that to grow gooseberries and currants successfully in a town environment they must be protected from birds who eat the potential fruit buds during the winter months. This necessitated the purchase of a large and expensive fruit cage to cover the growing area. It also proved necessary to keep the small mesh top net on during the winter, against the recommendations of the makers because of the risk of damage to the cage from a fall of snow. My luck held for several years, but one Sunday morning in mid April I came downstairs to find that a fall of very wet snow in the early hours had built up on the top net. While the net had held, the weight of snow had reduced the cage supports to a heap of twisted metal. The complete cage was never erected again. It had also become apparent that our family and friends could not possibly eat all the wonderfully flavoured dessert berries we were now producing, which when frozen lost their unique flavour and became mere culinary gooseberries.

I became more discriminating and gradually reduced the number of gooseberries grown. Then I began planting apple cordons along one of my perimeter borders. In time they proved very successful and the replacement of gooseberries with cordon apples and pears has continued. In the course of my fruit growing I bought various fruit books, among them the Fruit Yearbooks published for the Fruit Group by the Royal Horticultural Society between the years 1947 and 1956. In the Yearbook for 1951-52 there is an article entitled *The Fun of Finding Out* by the late Bernard Crewdson. This article fascinated me and has spurred me on to follow a similar path. Much of his experience and advice has proved very sound, and I would commend any fruit grower to read the Yearbooks.

For some years in addition to my garden I have had two allotments where, among other crops, I grow various rootstocks on which I graft fresh cultivars to try each year. My objective is to grow a range of choice apples and pears that will provide fruit all the year round. With apples, in a good year we can span the period from August to May. The pears will fruit from late July to February but the search for fruit perfection continues....

BOB SANDERS, a keen private fruit grower, is a member of the RHS Fruit Group Committee and of Brogdale Horticultural Trust Friends Working Party

Acknowledgements

The Royal Horticultural Society would like to thank the following for their permission to reproduce the photographs and illustrations in this book:

BLACK AND WHITE PHOTOGRAPHS
8 Horticulture Research International, East Malling; 75 The Royal Horticultural Society.

BLACK AND WHITE ILLUSTRATIONS
15, 16, 18, 20 The Royal Horticultural Society; 21 taken from the Wisley Handbook *Grapes Indoors and Out* (copyright Cassell plc); 31 Pauline Dean; 52, 55, 66, 92, 103 Barbara Hampton

COLOUR PHOTOGRAPHS
i The Royal Horticultural Society; ii ADAS; iii top and bottom Horticulture Research International East Malling; iii middle ADAS; iv Photos Horticultural ; v Peter Blackburne-Maze; vi top Derek St Romaine; vi bottom left Horticulture Research International, East Malling; vi bottom right Gerald Edwards; vii Peter Bauwens; viii Horticulture Research International, East Malling

Index

Actinidia:
arguta 76
deliciosa 76
Alston, Frank 110-13
Apple 35, 53-5
  Blenheim Orange 35
  Braeburn 16
  Bramley's Seedling 11, 12,
    43, 44, 54
  breeding disease and pest
    resistant cultivars 110-12
  Captain Kidd 35
  Cox's Orange Pippin 11, 35
    43, 54, 59, 78, 111, 116
  Crunchers 117
  D'Arcy Spice 35
  Devonshire Quarrenden
    121
  Egremont Russet 35
  Falstaff 11, 35, 110, 111
  Fiesta 110, 111, 112
  Florina 111
  Fortune 35
  Fuji 16
  Gala 16, 111
  Gascoyne's Scarlet 121
  Gavin 13
  Golden Delicious 15, 40, 11
  Greensleeves 11
  Hibernal 40
  Hunting Apple 121
  Idared 111
  Jonagold 11, 16, 44, 111
  Jonathan 111, 122
  Jupiter 35
  Kidd's Orange Red 35
  King Russet 35
  McIntosh 122
  Mirabelle 121
  new cultivars at HRI 112
  Northern Spy 42
  Orleans Reinette 35
  Pixie 35
  Queen Cox 54
  Red Pixie 35
  Reinette du Canada 16
  Ribston Pippin 35
  Spartan 35
  spraying crops 113-15
  Sunset 35, 78
  Warrior 72-4
  William Crump 35
  Worcester Pearmain 7
  Zoete Aagt 40
Arbury, Jim 74-8

Association of Pomologists,
  Germany 119
Atkins, David 113-16
Baker, Harry 33-6
Bauwens, Peter 25-9
Baxter, Sheila 22-5, 59-61,
  90-93
Bees 62-7
Berrie, Angela 93-102
Blackberry 82
  Ashton Cross 82
  Chehalem 82
  Darrow 82
  Loch Ness 80, 82
  Thornfree 82
Blackburne-Maze, Peter 14-18
Blackcurrant 33, 60, 82-3
  Baldwin 11, 34
  Ben Connan 83
  Ben Sarek 11, 34
  Ben series 82
  Blacksmith 34
  Boskoop Giant 34
  Raven 34
Blueberry 34, 76
  Berkeley 34
  Bluecrop 34
  Bluetta 77
  Earliblue 34
  Goldtraube 77
  Heerma 77
  Ivanhoe 77
  Patriot 77
Brogdale Horticultural Trust
  67-72
Cherry 36, 58
  Alfred 36
  Farmingdale 36
  Merchant 13
  Merton Glory 13
  Moor Park 36
  Morello 36
  Morrello type 49
  Stella 36, 76
Croquers de Pommes 117
Cross, Jerry 93-102
Cultivation of fruit 12
Cydonia oblonga 46
Disease:
  apple canker 97
  apple scab 96
  Botrytis cinerea 98
  *Chondrostereum pur
    pureum* (silver leaf) 104
  control 77-8

Disease
  Erwinia amylovora (fire
    blight) 45
  June Yellows 11
  Nectria 104
  of apples and pears 96-7
  Phytophthora root rot 86, 87
  Phytophthora cactorum
    (collar rot) 40
  plum pox virus 97
  Podosphaera leucotricha
    (apple mildew) 110, 111
  powdery mildew 97
  Pseudomonas species
    (bacterial canker) 49
  Taphrina deformans 77
  Venturia inaequalis
    (apple scab) 110
  verticillium wilt 98
Dodd, Peter 53-9
East Malling *see also*
  Horticultural Research
  International 5, 7, 8, 40,
  44, 47, 80, 85
Edwards, Gerald 51-3
Fructus, Switzerland 119
Fruit:
  cultivation 12
  grown organically 106-9
  Group of the RHS *see* RHS
    Fruit Group
  organic pest and disease
    control 108-9
  organic weed control 108
  pests and diseases 12-13
  soft, breeding of 79-84
  trees, wounds or decay
    of 103-5
Gage 36, 51-3
  Jefferson 36
  Old English Greengage 36
  Royale de Vilvoorde 36
  Willingham Gage 36
Gardens, Ryton Organic 106-9
Gooseberry 33
  Bedford Yellow 33
  Careless 124
  Early Green Hairy 33, 76
  Golden Drop 33, 76
  Greenfinch 13
  Invicta 13, 33
  Langley Gage 33, 76
  Leveller 124
  Lord Derby 76
  Martlet 109

Gooseberry
  Red Champagne 33, 76
  Thatcher 33
  Whinham's Industry
    33, 124
  Whitesmith 33
  Wisley 76
  Yellow Champagne 76
Grapes and Vines see also *Vitis*
  Black Corinth 25, 26
  Black Hamburgh 20, 21, 32
  Black Monukka 26, 28
  Boskoop Glory 25
  Buckland Sweetwater 20, 32
  Canadice Seedless 28
  commercial growing of 22-5
  Concord 28
  Concord Seedless 28
  Emerald Seedless 26
  Flame 28
  Foster's Seedling 20, 21, 32
  Glenora 27
  grown as standards 29-32
  grown under glass 18-21
  Himrod 25, 27, 28
  Interlaken 27, 28
  Lakemont 28
  Mars 27, 28
  Mrs Pearson 32
  Mrs Pince 32
  Muscat Champion 32
  Muscat Hamburgh 32
  Muscat of Alexandria 19,
    21, 32
  Perlette 27
  Pinot Noir 17
  Red Flame 25
  Reliance 28
  Ruby Seedless 26
  seedless 25-29
  Seyval 24
  Suffolk Red 28
  Thompson Seedless 25,
    26, 28
  trials 26-9
  Venus 28
  Wittle van der Laan 25
Greenwood, Pippa 103-6
Hatton, Christopher 7-8
Hatton, Sir Ronald 5
Henry Doubleday Research
  Association 106-9
Horticultural Research
  International (HRI) 44, 45,
    85, 86, 96-7, 98, 110
Integrated pest and disease
  management 93-102
Interstocks 39
Kiwi 76 *see also Actinidia*

Knight, Victoria 84-90
Loganberry 81
Lychee 123
Malus:
  floribunda 112
  robusta 111, 112
  zumi 111
Morus:
  alba 121
  nigra 121
McNicol, Ronnie 79-84
Morgan, Joan 67-72
National Fruit Collections,
  Brogdale, Kent 117
National Orchard Foundation,
  Belgium 118
Northern Pomological
  Association, Holland 118
Orchard design 53-59
Peach 36
  Duke of York 36
  Lord Napier 36
  Peregrine 36
Pear 56-7
  Beurré Hardy 39
  Concorde 16, 35
  Conference 35, 56, 59, 60
  Doyenné du Comice 11,
    15, 16, 35, 56
  Gala 16
  Laxton's Superb 123
  Merton Pride 35
  Olivier de Serres 35
  Onward 35
  Williams' Bon Chrètien 11,
    16, 35, 39, 56, 123
Pépinières du Valois 16
Pests and diseases:
  Amphorophora idaei 86
  apple rust mite 95
  Byturus tomentosus 85
  codling moth 94
  Damson hop aphid 97
  Dysaphis plantaginea (rosy
    apple aphid) 110
  Eriosma lanigerum (apple
    aphid) 42
  in apple orchards 99-102
  of fruit 12-13
  Otiorhynchus sulcatus 77
  Phorodon humuli 97
  Phytoseiulus persimilis 77
  Plasmopara viticola 27
  red spider mite 95
  rust mites 97
  summer fruit tortrix moth
    95
  Tetranychus urticae 77
  tortrix moths 94

Pest control 77-8
  Anthocorid 95
  Phytoseiulus persimilis 98
  Steinernema carpocase 92
  Typhlodromus pyri 95
Pink currant Champagne
  34, 76
Plum 36, 51-3, 57
  Cambridge Gage 52
  Coe's Golden Drop 36
  cordons 51-3
  Czar 52
  Denniston's Superb 52
  Edwards 52
  Giant Prune 51, 52
  Imperial Gage 52
  Kirke's Blue 36, 51
  Marjorie's Seedling 11, 51,
    57
  Merchant 12
  Old Greengage 51
  Oullins Gage 52
  Reeves Seedling 36
  Shropshire Damson 52
  Stella 12
  Victoria 11, 48, 49, 52, 57
Potager du Roi 14-16
Prunus:
  avium 39, 49, 58
  cerasifera 48
    x *munsoniana* 48
  cerasus 49
  x *dawyckensis* 49
  domestica 48
  fruticosa 49
  incisa 49
  insititia 48
  mahaleb 49
  mugus 49
  persica platycarpa 36
Pyrus:
  betulifolia 46
  calleryana 46
  communis 46
  pyrifolia 46
  serotina 35
  ussuriensis 46
Raspberry 34 60, 80
  Admiral 34
  Allgold 86
  Amity 87
  Autumn Bliss 11, 34, 85,
    86, 87, 88, 90
  Autumn Britten 85-6, 87
  Autumn Cascade 86
  Bogong 86, 88
  collection at Wisley 76
  Dinkum 86, 87, 88
  Falbrook 87

Raspberry
  Glen Clova 80
  Glen Garry 81
  Glen Lyon 81
  Glen Magna 81
  Glen Moy 34, 80
  Glen Prosen 34, 80
  Glen Rosa 81
  Glen Shee 81
  Glencoe 82
  Goldie 86
  Heritage 85, 86, 87
  Joan Squire 86, 87
  Joe Mello 87
  Kiwigold 86
  Leo 11, 34, 81
  Lloyd George 34
  Malling Delight 81
  Malling Jewel 11, 34
  Newton Wonder 122
  Norfolk Giant 11
  Perrons Red 87
  Polana 86, 87
  primocane fruiting 84-90
  production 88
  Red River 87
  Redsetter 34
  Redwing 87
  Ruby 87
  September 85
  Sweetbriar 87
  Terri-Louise 86, 87
  The Devon 122
  Zeva Herbsternte 85
Redcurrant 34
  Jonkheer van Tets 34
  Rivers Late Red 76
  Stanza 34
RHS, Fruit Group 5, 9-10
RHS Wisley, model fruit
  gardens 74-9
Rootstock:
  Adams 332 46
  apple, from around the
    world 44
  BA29 46
  Blue Tit 77
  BP-1 (B13) 47
  Bramley's Seedling 43
  Brompton 48
  Brossier Series 47
  Charger 49
  clonal 39
    for apple 40
    for cherry 49
    for pears 45
    for plums 48
    for quince 46

Rootstock
  Colt 12, 50, 58
  CTS 212 47
  Czar 77
  Damas C 48
  Damil 50
  dwarfing 77
  East Malling Long Ashton
    Scheme 41
  Edabriz/Tabel 50
  EMLA M9 41
  Ferlenain 48, 49
  F12/1 12, 58
  Inmil 50
  history and development
    of 37-8
  M1 41
  M2 12, 41, 54
  M3 41
  M4 41
  M6 41
  M7 40, 41, 78
  M8 41, 43
  M9 12, 39, 40, 41, 43,
    45, 56
  M25 43
  M26 43, 44, 54
  M27 12, 39, 43, 44, 76, 77
  M29 56
  Mahaleb 49
  Marianna 48
  Maridon 49
  Mazzard 49
  Mazzard F12/1 49
  Merton 793 42
  MM104 42
  MM106 39, 40, 41, 42,
    43, 54
  MM109 42
  MM111 39, 41, 42, 43
  Myrobalan B 48, 57
  OHF333 47
  Pershore 38, 48, 57
  Pixy 12, 48, 49, 51, 57, 77
  Pontaris 39
  Pontavium 39
  Pyrus 46, 47
  Pyrus clonal 48
  Pyrus communis 47
  Quince 39
  Quince A 56
  Quince C 56
  Quince Fontenay 15
  raised from seed 38-9
  St Julien A 48, 57
  St Lucie 64 49
  Sydo 46
  Weiroot 50

Rubus arcticus subsp.
    stellarcticus 76
Sale, John 72-4
Sanders, Bob 121-25
Scottish Crop Research
    Institute 61, 79-84
Self, Brian 5
Sherman, Bob 106-9
Showler, Karl 62-7
Society of German
    Pomologists 119
Société Pomologique du
    Berry 117
Strawberries 33, 61, 83
  Aromel 33
  Cambridge Favourite 11
  Cambridge Late Pine 33
  Climax 11
  Domanil 11
  Elsanta 11, 83, 98
  growing on raised beds
    90-93
  Hapil 33
  Huxley 11
  Honeyoe 33
  Melody 80
  Royal Sovereign 11, 33
  Symphony 33, 83
  Tenira 33
Stringer, Howard 117-120
Tayberry 75, 81
Tummelberry 75, 82
Vines see also *Vitis* and Grapes
  Double Guyot system of
    growing 22
  for table decoration 30-2
  grown in greenhouses
    18-21
  Geneva Double Curtain
    system 22
Vitis
  labrusca 26
  vinifera 24, 26
    x *V. amurensis* 24
Whitecurrant:
  collection at Wisley 76
  Jonkheer van Tets 76
  Raby Castle 76
  Rovada 76
  Stanza 76
  Versailles Blanche 76
  White Grape 34
Windbreaks, use of for
  fruit growing 59-61
Waite, Ray 18-21, 29-32
Webster, Tony 37-50
Woodward, Jack 10-13